The Way to Pass

Maths

GCSE
Foundation Level

The Way to Pass
National Curriculum
Maths

GCSE
Foundation Level

Arnold Burdett

VERMILION
LONDON

First published in 1994

3 5 7 9 10 8 6 4

Text copyright © Rockhopper 1994

First published in the United Kingdom in 1994
by Vermilion
an imprint of Ebury Press
Random House, 20 Vauxhall Bridge Road,
London SW1V 2SA

Random House Australia (Pty) Limited
20 Alfred Street, Milsons Point, Sydney,
New South Wales 2061, Australia

Random House New Zealand Limited
18 Poland Road, Glenfield,
Auckland 10, New Zealand

Random House South Africa (Pty) Limited
Endulini, 5A Jubilee Road, Parktown 2193,
South Africa

Random House UK Limited Reg. No. 954009

Editor: Alison Wormleighton
Design: Jerry Goldie Graphic Design

A CIP catalogue record for this book
is available from the British Library

ISBN 0-09-178123-X

Typeset by AFS Image Setters Ltd, Glasgow
Printed in Great Britain by Butler & Tanner Ltd,
London and Frome

oreword

elcome to THE WAY TO PASS MATHS GCSE FOUNDATION LEVEL. I want to tell
u why I have put together this series of books, along with a team of teachers,
visers and examiners.

A lot of people don't enjoy Maths because they're frightened of it. I can
derstand how frightening it can be because I've been scared of it myself at
nes: maybe the teacher goes through the work a little too quickly for you,
aybe there are too many children in your class, maybe you're not the best at
aths in your class. All of these reasons can make Maths seem impossible. What I
ve learned through the years is that the more help you have and the longer
u spend on something, the more likely you are to get over any difficulties.

If you're studying for GCSE Foundation Level, then you will already know that
e highest grade you can achieve is Grade D, which is well worth trying for.
hatever you might think about school, and about Maths in particular, there is
doubt that Maths and English are the two most important subjects for you to
well in. If you understand most of what you're taught, you are set for a
ghter future, being able to do some of the things you've always wanted to.
e WAY TO PASS can help you through your GCSE courses, making the subjects
u're taught a little more understandable and interesting, making your exams
sier and helping you to get the best grades possible.

All of the books are based around work for you to do at home. Most of the
planations will have been covered in classes at school and so you won't want
wade through pages and pages of more explanations. That is why in each
ction we give you a concise list of the main things you need to know, and then
ork through exercises to practise each one.

This completely new range of books has been organised so that, if you want
, you can follow the already successful VIDEO CLASS videos covering the same
bjects/levels. All of the book sections work together neatly with the video
ctions so that you have a complete course at your fingertips. Alternatively, the
oks can be used on their own, without the videos.

I certainly hope that this series will make Maths and English more
proachable and slightly friendlier than they were before. Remember, you must
llow what is taught in school and do as many exercises as you can—the more
actice you get, the better you will be.

Carol Vorderman

Contents

The National Curriculum

The National Curriculum sets targets for pupils of all abilities from age 5 to 16, specifying what they should know, understand and be able to do at each stage of their education. It is divided into four **Key Stages**: Key Stage 1 (age 5–7), Key Stage 2 (age 7–11), Key Stage 3 (age 11–14) and Key Stage 4 (age 14–16).

At the end of Key Stages 1, 2 and 3, pupils take national tests in the **core subjects**: Maths and English (at age 7, 11 and 14) and Science (at age 11 and 14). At the end of Key Stage 4 (age 16) the **GCSE examinations** are the main way of assessing children's progress.

Whereas in the tests at Key Stages 1, 2 and 3 children achieve particular **Levels**, moving up one Level every two years or so, in the GCSE examination they are graded from A (at the top) to G (at the lower end of the scale). The grade A* may be awarded for exceptional achievement. U stands for ungraded or unclassified.

Nearly all pupils take GCSE examinations in Maths and in English. There are different **tiers** of paper to suit the varying capabilities of the pupils, and the grading system reflects the difficulty of the papers taken. Teachers decide which level is best suited to each pupil, who then has a clearly defined target to aim for

THE WAY TO PASS books are all based on National Curriculum requirements. The GCSE English book covers the main elements of the syllabus at each tier, while GCSE Maths is split into three different books – Foundation, Intermediate and Higher – corresponding to the three tiers of the examination papers. The books will serve as a valuable back-up to a child's classwork and homework and provide an excellent preparation for the GCSE examinations.

Introduction

When you are studying for GCSE examinations, you are often looking for that extra bit of help. The WAY TO PASS series is designed to help you learn the facts and put them into practice, revising at your own pace and concentrating on the areas you need to work on most. This book is aimed at Foundation Level (also sometimes known as Basic Level, or 'P' Level), which covers grades D–G.

Revision should not be rushed. Try to devise a revision timetable, spending about a week on one or two sections. First, check that you know all the facts set out under **Things You Need to Know** in each section. Next, work through the **How to Do It** questions, which are worked examples showing you how to answer each type of question relating to that section. Cover each solution as you do it, then check to see you have answered it correctly. When you feel confident that you have understood the work in that section, try the **Do It Yourself** questions. You'll find the **Answers** near the end of the book.

The numbering system used in the book makes it easy for you to concentrate on whatever topics you feel you most need to revise. Each topic within a section has a number, which identifies that topic throughout the section. Thus, in Section , for example, an explanation of rounding numbers appears in no. 1 of Things You Need to Know; then exercise 1 of How to Do It shows you how to answer questions involving rounding numbers; and finally you can check how well you understand rounding numbers with Do It Yourself exercises 1a, 1b, 1c and 1d.

You do not have to work through the book in any particular order; indeed you should spend more time revising topics you are not very good at. However, sections 2, 7, 11 and 16 – the sections on number patterns, the metric system, angles and algebra – are particularly important.

About a week before the examination, you can attempt the **Sample Exam Paper** at the end of the book. It is made up of the type of questions you will get in the actual exam, and should take you about one to one-and-a-half hours to do. You can check your solutions with those at the back of the book. If it were a real GCSE exam, you'd need to get about three-quarters of the questions correct to reach grade D standard. If there are topics you are still weak in, go back and look at these before the exam.

In the actual examination, do not spend too long on any one question. You can always go back if you have time at the end. Make sure that your solutions are easy to follow and neatly written out. Do not leave out essential working. You will lose marks if a question asks you to show your working and you give only the answer.

Try to enjoy your revision. You will be surprised how this helps. Don't leave it to the last minute before your exam. Remember, the more you practise, the better you will cope.

Number Work

Things You Need to Know

1 How to **round numbers**. The rule is to look at the first figure that will be ignored after the rounding – if it is 5 or higher, then the figure before it is increased by 1, otherwise the figure before it is left as it is. For example:

34.8 = 35 to the nearest whole number   (the 8 increases the 4 to 5)

95.21 = 95.2 to one decimal place   (the 1 is not big enough to alter the 2)

149.7 = 150 to the nearest whole number   (take care – the 7 increases the 9 to 10, hence the answer)

27.96 = 28.0 to one decimal place (1 d.p.)

2 **Factors** are numbers which divide exactly into the given number. The factors of 18 are 1 2 3 6 and 9. If you divide 18 by any of these, your calculator will give you a whole number, not a decimal. Two, or more, numbers can have a factor or factors in common. For example:

Factors of 20 are: 1 2 4 5 10

Factors of 32 are: 1 2 4 8 16

Factors of 56 are: 1 2 4 7 8 14 28

So 2 and 4 are **common factors** of 20, 32 and 56. (1 is not usually listed.) Their highest common factor (**HCF**) is 4.

3 A **prime number** is a number that has only two factors – 1 and itself (or to put it another way, there aren't two whole numbers both greater than 1 that multiply to give the number). For example, 59 is a prime number; 1 and 59 are the only numbers that divide exactly into 59.

Some of the factors of a number will be prime numbers. For example:

The factors of 56 are: 1   2   4   7   8   14   28

But the only **prime factors** of 56 are 2 and 7. (1 does not count as a prime number.)

4 The **multiples** of a number are simply the results for the multiplication table of that number. The multiples of 4, for example, are:

4   8   12   16   20   24   28   32

One important group of multiples is the multiples of 2 – they are called **even numbers**. If a number is not in the even numbers it is called an **odd number**.

5 **Negative** numbers simply tell us how far below some zero mark we have gone. They are used quite a lot with temperature, money (particularly bank accounts!), years before and after the birth of Christ (BC and AD), the height of a river (above/below some average level) and so on.

Here are some examples of arithmetic with positive and negative numbers:

Addition

$$(+7)+(+3) = (+10)$$
$$(+8)+(-4) = (+4)$$
$$(+5)+(-10) = (-5)$$
$$(-4)+(-3) = (-7)$$

Subtraction

$$(+10)-(+4) = (+6)$$
$$(+12)-(-3) = (+12)+3$$
$$= (+15)$$
$$(-4)-(-7) = (-4)+7$$
$$= (+3)$$
$$(-3)-(+6) = (-3)-6$$
$$= (-9)$$

Multiplication

(Remember that when the signs are the same, the result is positive and when the signs are different the result is negative.)

$$(+6) \times (+5) = (+30)$$
$$(+4) \times (-3) = (-12)$$
$$(-8) \times (+5) = (-40)$$
$$(-5) \times (-9) = (+45)$$

Division

(The rule here is the same rule as for multiplication.)

$$(+12) \div (-3) = (-4)$$
$$(-30) \div (-5) = (+6)$$
$$(+24) \div (+8) = (+3)$$
$$(-48) \div (+6) = (-8)$$

'It's a good idea to memorise the squares of the numbers 1 to 10'

6 When we multiply a number by itself we call it **squaring** the number. For example, the square of 7 is 49 (because $7 \times 7 = 49$).

The **square root** of a number is the reverse of this – so the square root of 49 is 7. We can write this as

$$7^2 = 49$$

square root of 49 = 7   It is often written as $\sqrt{49} = 7$

With **cubing** we extend the idea by multiplying the number by itself three times. For example, 5 cubed is $5 \times 5 \times 5$ which is 125. Similarly the cube root of 125 is 5. This would be written as

$$5^3 = 125$$

cube root of 125 = 5   It is often written as $\sqrt[3]{125} = 5$

Remember: the root sign is like a bracket; everything inside needs working out before the root is found.

$$\sqrt{2 \times 3 + 5 \times 6} = \sqrt{6 + 30}$$
$$= \sqrt{36}$$
$$= 6$$

Not all numbers give nice, neat answers for the roots – many will have lots of decimal places. (Scientific calculators have buttons for finding roots and they give the answer to lots of decimal places – now you know one reason that we need to be able to round the answer.)

How to Do It

1 Round the number 184.3576 to:
   (i) the nearest hundred;   (ii) the nearest ten;
  (iii) the nearest whole number;   (iv) two decimal places.

Solution

  (i) $184.3756 = 200$ (to the nearest hundred)
  (ii) $184.3756 = 180$ (to the nearest ten)
 (iii) $184.3756 = 184$ (to the nearest whole number)
 (iv) $184.3756 = 184.38$ (to two decimal places)

2a What are the factors of 36?

Solution
The factors of 36 are   1 2 3 4 6 9 12 and 18

b What are the common factors of 28 and 70?

Solution
The factors of 28 are   1 2 4 7 14
The factors of 70 are   1 2 5 7 10 14 35
So the common factors are   2 7 and 14
(Clearly 1 is also a common factor, but often this is not listed.)

3a Which of the numbers from 10 to 20 inclusive are prime?

Solution

10	not prime (5×2)	11	prime
12	not prime ($4 \times 3, 2 \times 6$)	13	prime
14	not prime (2×7)	15	not prime (5×3)
16	not prime ($2 \times 8, 4 \times 4$)	17	prime
18	not prime ($3 \times 6, 9 \times 2$)	19	prime
20	not prime ($2 \times 10, 5 \times 4$)		

(You need to find only *one* pair of numbers that multiply for the number not to be prime.)

b What are the prime factors of 60?

Solution
The factors of 60 are   1   2   3   4   5   6   10   12   15   20   30
The prime factors are   2   3 and 5

4 **a** Write down the multiples of 2 which are less than 25. What do you notice about the units figure?

Solution
The multiples of 2 less than 25 are

2   4   6   8   10   12   14   16   18   20   22 and 24

The units figures go in order   2   4   6   8   0   2   4   6   8   0   and so on.

b (i) What are the multiples of 3 between 20 and 35?
(ii) Which of the multiples in (i) are also even?

Solution

(i) The multiples of 3 between 20 and 35 are   21   24   27   30 and 33.
(ii) The even multiples are 24 and 30.

5 **a** On the number line below put a cross below the numbers 3, -4, 0, 5, -1:

Solution

b In my bank account I now have £75.00, but last week I had $-$£30.00 (I owed the bank £30.00). How much has been paid in during the week?

Solution
I owed the bank £30.00 and now have £75.00, so £105.00 must have been paid in (£30.00 to cover the debt and £75.00 over and above that).

5 Find the value of:
  (i) 8^2
  (ii) square root of 100
  (iii) 10^3
  (iv) the cube root of 343
  (v) the square root of 1234 correct to two decimal places
  (vi) the cube root of 4567 correct to the nearest whole number

Solution

  (i) $8^2 = 8 \times 8 = 64$
  (ii) square root of 100 $= 10$ (because $10 \times 10 = 100$)
  (iii) $10^3 = 10 \times 10 \times 10 = 1000$
  (iv) cube root of 343 $= 7$ (use a calculator)
  (v) square root of 1234 $= 35.128\,336$ (on your calculator, the answer might differ slightly at the last figure, or have more figures)

$= 35.13$ (correct to two decimal places)
  (vi) cube root 4567 $= 16.591\,17$ (again, might differ on your calculator)

$= 17$ (correct to the nearest whole number)

Do It Yourself

1 a Write each of the following numbers:
   (i) correct to the nearest 100
   (ii) correct to three significant figures
   (iii) correct to two decimal places

9326.686   85.513   227.245

b Write each of the following numbers to two decimal places:

   (i) square root of 7   (ii) $2 \times$ square root of 11
   (iii) $5 \div 9$ (iv) 3.142^2

c Alison divides £50 by 14 using her calculator. The display shows 3.571 428 571. What is the answer to the nearest penny?

d The report on the local football match said that 27 000 people had attended, correct to the nearest thousand.
   (i) What is the largest number that could have been present?
   (ii) What is the smallest number that could have been present?

2 a Which of the following numbers are factors of 24:

2, 3, 4, 5, 6, 9, 12, 18, 48, 96

b (i) Write down all the factors of 40.
(ii) What factors does 40 have in common with the number 56?

3 a Write down two prime numbers whose sum is 16 and whose product is 55.

b Write down two prime numbers whose difference is 2 and whose product is 35.

4 a Write down the first 12 multiples of 3 in a line. Underneath each of the multiples write the figure down if it is a single figure *or* write the result of adding the two figures if it is two figures. What do you notice?

b (i) Write down the multiples of 7 which are less than 100.
(ii) Write down the even multiples of 7 from the list. What multiples are they, apart from 7?

5 Work out:

(i) $-11+7$ (ii) $-8+(-6)$ (iii) $7-(-2)$ (iv) $6 \div (-3)$
(v) $(-4) \times (-7)$ (vi) $-21 \div 3$

6 a Without the aid of a calculator, say which two whole numbers the following lie between. The first two have been done for you.

(i) $\sqrt{200}$ between 14 and 15 (since $14^2 = 196$ and $15^2 = 225$)
(ii) 2.4^2 between 4 and 9 (since $2^2 = 4$ and $3^2 = 9$)
(iii) $\sqrt{40}$ (iv) $\sqrt{27.3}$ (v) $\sqrt[3]{100}$
(vi) $\sqrt[3]{180}$ (vii) 5.7^2 (viii) 8.9^2

b Find the following, using a calculator only if you really need to.

(i) $\sqrt{3^2+4^2}$ (ii) $\sqrt{5^2-4^2}$ (iii) $\sqrt{13^2-5^2}$
(iv) $\sqrt{5^2+12^2}$

Number Patterns

Things You Need to Know

1 How to spot number patterns in order to be able to predict subsequent numbers in a list or to say if a number belongs with the others. To spot a number pattern, you need to be able to 'see' more than just the numbers. The things to look for are:

- Is there a connection between one number and the next? Look at the difference between neighbouring numbers.
- Is there anything special about the numbers? For example, do they all divide by 5?
- Are the numbers 'shape numbers'? Does that number of dots form a special shape?

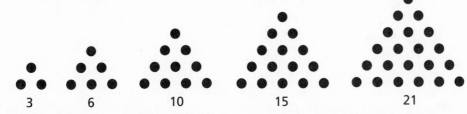

1   3   6   10   15   21

2 **Triangular numbers** are an example of 'shape numbers'. When the number of dots is put down it can form a triangle – like stacking cans on a shelf. The first six triangular numbers are shown above.

'It is possible to invent further 'shape numbers', but the triangular and square numbers are the best known'

3 **Square numbers** are those numbers that form a square when put down in dots. They are also those numbers that have a whole number as the square root. For example, the fourth square number is 16 (4 × 4), as shown in the diagram on the right.

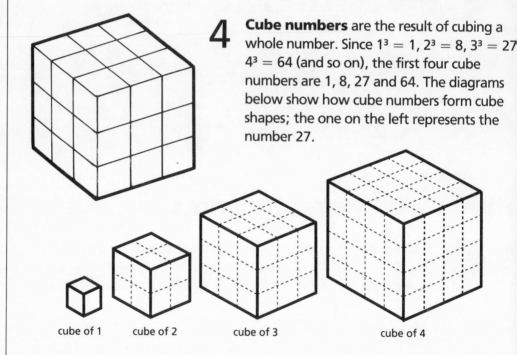

4 **Cube numbers** are the result of cubing a whole number. Since $1^3 = 1$, $2^3 = 8$, $3^3 = 27$ $4^3 = 64$ (and so on), the first four cube numbers are 1, 8, 27 and 64. The diagrams below show how cube numbers form cube shapes; the one on the left represents the number 27.

cube of 1   cube of 2   cube of 3   cube of 4

5 **Fibonacci numbers** belong to a sequence in which the next number is the result of adding the two numbers immediately before it:

1   1   2   3   5   8   13   and so on

There are many patterns in a sequence of Fibonacci numbers, and it arises in a lot of situations. It is also an example of a simple rule giving the next number. However, it is not easy to tell if a particular number is in the sequence. For example, is 123 a Fibonacci number? No, but you can only tell by working through the list until you get a number bigger than 123!

5 When we are investigating number patterns, we look for:
- a rule for continuing the sequence
- the rule for producing a number
- whether the sequence is limited, or goes on for ever.

How to Do It

Here are some examples of number patterns. What are the missing numbers?

(i) 5   10   15   20   25   30   35   40 ...
(ii) $\frac{1}{2}$ $\frac{1}{4}$ $\frac{1}{8}$ $\frac{1}{16}$ $\frac{1}{32}$ $\frac{1}{64}$ ...
(iii) 1   2   4   7   11   16   22 ...

Solution

(i) These numbers go up in 5s, so the missing numbers are 25 and 40.
(ii) The denominator (bottom part) of the fraction is multiplied by 2, so the missing numbers are $\frac{1}{16}$ and $\frac{1}{64}$.
(iii) The difference between successive numbers increases by 1 each time, so the missing numbers are 7 and 22.

2 Show that the following numbers are triangular numbers and say which triangular number each one is:

(i) 10   (ii) 3   (iii) 36

  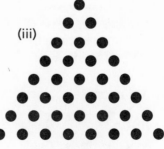

Solution

(i)

Fourth triangular number

(ii)

Second triangular number

(iii)

Eighth triangular number

3   (i) What is the eighth square number?   - 64

      (ii) Show in two ways that 36 is a square number.   6×6

Solution

(i) The eighth square number is $8 \times 8 = 64$.

(ii) 36 is 6×6 so it is a square number (the sixth one).

     This can also be seen in the diagram on the right.

4   Continue the following cube number sequence:

       1   8   27   64   125

What do you notice about the fourth cube number?

Solution

     The next cube number is $4 \times 4 \times 4 = 64$

     and the next one is $5 \times 5 \times 5 = 125$ 216   343   512   729

The fourth cube number is also a square number. Can you find the next cube number that is also a square number? Do you make it 729?

5   Write down the Fibonacci series up to the tenth term. Take four numbers next to each other and write them down in order:

     1   1   2   3   5   8   13   21   34   55

     a   *b*   *c*   *d*

Multiply the outer pair (*a* and *d*) and multiply the inner pair (*b* and *c*).

(i) What is the difference between the answers?

(ii) Do it twice more. What do you notice?

Solution

     1   1   2   3   5   8   13   21   34   55

(i) 1   1   2   3

     Outer pair are 1 and 3; this gives 3.

     Inner pair are 1 and 2; this gives 2.

     Difference is 1.

(ii) 3   5   8   13

   Outer pair are 3 and 13; this gives 39.

   Inner pair are 5 and 8; this gives 40.

   Difference is 1.

   13   21   34   55

   Outer pair are 13 and 55; this gives 715.

   Inner pair are 21 and 34; this gives 714.

   Difference is 1.

The difference is always 1.

Here is a rule for producing a sequence of numbers:

'Start off with the number 1, then to get the next number subtract 1, to get the next number after that add 3; now repeat the process of subtracting 1 for the next number and then adding 3 for the one after that.'

What is the tenth number in the series?

Solution

1   0   3   2   5   4   7   6   9   8   11   10   13   12   and so on

The tenth number is the number 8.

   This could be thought of as the odd numbers (1   3   5   7   9 . . .) with the even numbers (and zero) in-between (0   2   4   6   8   10 . . .).

Do It Yourself

a Write down the next two numbers in each of the sequences:

   (i) 3   6   9   12   15   18 ✓   (ii) 4   8   16   32   64   128 ✓

   (iii) 2   7   13   20   28   37   47 ✓   (iv) 64   32   16   8   4   2 ✓

b The first five numbers in a series of numbers are

   5   13   25   41   61   85   113 ✓✓

   (i) Which of these numbers are (a) prime numbers, (b) square numbers?

   (ii) Write down the difference (in order) between neighbouring numbers.

   (iii) Write down the next two numbers of the series.

2 Write down the first six triangular numbers. Which of these numbers are

  (i) prime numbers   (ii) multiples of 5   (iii) multiples of 3

(handwritten) 1 3 6 10 15 21 28/ 1.3 √ / 10 15 √ 3.6 15 21 √

3 If S_1 means the first square number (i.e. 1^2), S_2 means the second square number (i.e. 2^2) and so on, answer each of the following questions using this shorthand; the answers are all square numbers.

  (i) $2 \times S_1 + 2$ (ii) $S_3 + S_4$ (iii) $2 \times S_1 + S_3 + S_5$ (iv) $S_3 + S_4 + S_5 - S_1$

(handwritten) 4 or S_2 25 or S_5 36 or S_6 49 or S_7

4 Here are the first few cube numbers and underneath are the differences between neighbouring numbers. This is then repeated until we appear always to get the number 6.

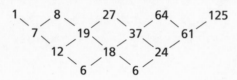

If this is 'reversed', we can extend the table:

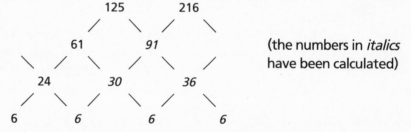

(the numbers in *italics* have been calculated)

Continue extending the table until you have the eleventh number across the top. Is this number 11^3?

(handwritten) 216 343 512 729 1000 1331 YES √
361 87 42 169 48 217 54 271 60 331 √
64 125 91
61 1 30
6 4

(left margin handwritten) 19 343 ? 165 or
64 125 91 216 343
61 1 30 361 87
30

5 Take any three neighbouring numbers in the Fibonacci Series, such as 2 3 5. Multiply the outer pair of numbers (2 and 5 in this example) and square the middle number (3 in this example). Do this for five sets of three Fibonacci numbers. What do you notice?

(left margin handwritten) 1 1 2 3 5 8 13
19 49 129
10 9 24 25 65 64

6 Write down the numbers represented by the question marks in each of the following sequences of numbers. Give a reason for your answer.

(handwritten annotation) 36 49, number halves down ÷2 8 4
(handwritten) up odd nu

  (i) 1 4 9 16 25 ? ? √   (ii) 512 256 128 64 32 16 ? ?/ √
  (iii) 13 26 52 ? 208 ? doubles
  (handwritten) 104
  13 26 52 104 √

Fractions

3

Things You Need to Know

1 A **fraction** is a way of saying how much of the whole piece you wish to have or use. You might cut a cake up into four equal size pieces and eat just one of the pieces – you would have eaten $\frac{1}{4}$ of the cake. A fraction has two parts:

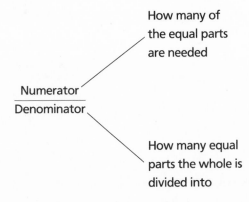

How many of
the equal parts
are needed

Numerator
Denominator

How many equal
parts the whole is
divided into

2 Some fractions are equal to each other – they are called **equivalent fractions**:

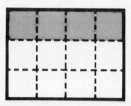 $\dfrac{4}{12}$ is the same as $\dfrac{1}{3}$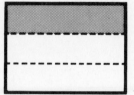

We can find equivalent fractions by multiplying the numerator and the denominator by the same number

$$\frac{1}{4} = \frac{2}{8} = \frac{3}{12} = \frac{4}{16} = \frac{5}{20} \cdots = \frac{100}{400} \cdots$$

3 As some fractions are equivalent to others we usually write down the simplest form (the one with the smallest numerator). We can do this by looking for common factors between the numerator and the denominator and cancelling:

$$\frac{40}{60} = \frac{4}{6} \text{ (we divided by 10)}$$

$$= \frac{2}{3} \text{ (we divided by 2)}$$

4 If the numerator is bigger than the denominator, this is called an **improper fraction**:

$$\frac{14}{5} = 1 + \frac{9}{5} \quad \left(\text{since } \frac{5}{5} = 1 \right)$$

$$= 1 + 1 + \frac{4}{5}$$

$$= 2\frac{4}{5}$$

'Be careful about writing mixed numbers. It is easy to put $3\frac{4}{7}$ but read and use it as $\frac{34}{7}$. Obviously they are not the same '

5 A number like $2\frac{4}{5}$ is a **mixed number** (a mix of a whole number and a fraction). It can be changed into an improper fraction:

$$3\frac{4}{7} = \frac{21}{7} + \frac{4}{7} \quad \left(\text{since a whole one is 7/7 then 3 must be } \frac{21}{7} \right)$$

$$= \frac{25}{7}$$

5 To add (or subtract) fractions they have to have the same denominator. If they are different, we have to change them (like if we tried to add $2.40 and 27 pesetas – we would have to change them into the same sort of currency). Equivalent fractions are used to do this: for example, for $\frac{3}{10}+\frac{1}{4}$ the **common denominator** is 20. (Because this is the smallest number that both 10 and 4 divide into, it is called the **least common denominator**, or **lowest common multiple**.)

$$\frac{3}{10}+\frac{1}{4}=\frac{3}{10}\times\frac{2}{2}+\frac{1}{4}\times\frac{5}{5}$$

$$=\frac{6}{20}+\frac{5}{20}$$

$$=\frac{11}{20}$$

'If you can't see a common denominator, simply multiply them together – we could have used 40, but then we would have had to cancel the fraction'

7 Multiplying two fractions together is done just as you might expect – you multiply the two numerators and multiply the two denominators:

$$\frac{2}{5}\times\frac{15}{16}=\frac{30}{80}\quad\text{(now cancel by dividing by 10)}$$

$$=\frac{3}{8}$$

8 To divide fractions you simply turn the dividing fraction upside down and then multiply instead of divide.

$$\frac{2}{3}\div\frac{8}{9}=\frac{2}{3}\times\frac{9}{8}$$

$$=\frac{18}{24}\quad\text{(now divide by 2)}$$

$$=\frac{9}{12}\quad\text{(now divide by 3)}$$

$$=\frac{3}{4}\quad\text{(you could have divided by 6 straightaway instead of 2 and then 3, but you don't have to).}$$

'Multiplying by $\frac{1}{2}$ is exactly the same as dividing by 2'

9 Fractions are often used to indicate parts of a quantity. For example, if you have a recipe for six people and you wish to make it for just two persons, then the quantities involved will be $\frac{1}{3}$ of the original quantities.

How to Do It

1 A slab of chocolate is divided into 12 equal pieces. If you eat 5 of these pieces what fraction of the slab of chocolate is left?

Solution

There are 7 pieces left out of the original 12 so the fraction remaining is $\frac{7}{12}$.

2 Give two more equivalent fractions for each of the following:

(i) $\frac{2}{3}$ (ii) $\frac{5}{11}$ (iii) $\frac{1}{4}$

Solution

There are many possible answers – but here are some:

(i) $\frac{2}{3} = \frac{4}{6} = \frac{20}{30}$ (ii) $\frac{5}{11} = \frac{15}{33} = \frac{20}{44}$ (iii) $\frac{1}{4} = \frac{4}{16} = \frac{12}{48}$

3 Simplify each of the following fractions:

(i) $\frac{8}{12}$ (ii) $\frac{9}{21}$ (iii) $\frac{36}{72}$

Solution

(i) $\frac{8}{12} = \frac{2}{3}$ (we divided by 4)   (ii) $\frac{9}{21} = \frac{3}{7}$ (we divided by 3)

(iii) $\frac{36}{72} = \frac{4}{8}$ (we divided by 9)

$= \frac{1}{2}$ (then we divided by 4)

4 What is the improper fraction $\frac{27}{5}$ as a mixed number?

Solution

5 lots of $\frac{1}{5}$ make a whole one so in $\frac{27}{5}$ there are 5 whole ones:

$$\frac{27}{5} = 5 \text{ whole ones and } \frac{2}{5} = 5\frac{2}{5}$$

5 What is $4\frac{2}{3}$ as an improper fraction?

Solution

$$4\frac{2}{3} = \frac{12}{3} + \frac{2}{3} = \frac{14}{3}$$

6 What is

(i) $\frac{1}{3} + \frac{1}{4}$ (ii) $\frac{3}{4} - \frac{5}{9}$

Solution

Remember that we have to make the fractions in each part into the same sort of fraction:

(i) $\frac{1}{3} + \frac{1}{4} = \frac{4}{12} + \frac{3}{12}$ (the smallest number that 4 and 3 both divide into is 12)

$$= \frac{7}{12}$$

(ii) $\frac{3}{4} - \frac{5}{9} = \frac{27}{36} - \frac{20}{36}$ (the smallest number that both 4 and 9 divide into is 36)

$$= \frac{7}{36}$$

7 What is the result of $\frac{4}{5} \times \frac{15}{16}$?

Solution

$$\frac{4}{5} \times \frac{15}{16} = \frac{60}{80} = \frac{6}{8} = \frac{3}{4}$$

8 What is $\frac{3}{8} \div \frac{1}{4}$?

Solution

$$\frac{3}{8} \div \frac{1}{4} = \frac{3}{8} \times \frac{4}{1} = \frac{12}{8} = \frac{3}{2} = 1\frac{1}{2}$$

9 A man leaves a quarter of his money to his wife, and the remainder is equally divided between his son and daughter. What fraction does each child get? If each child receives £6000, how much does his wife receive?

Solution $\frac{3}{8}$ 4000

If the man leaves a quarter to his wife this means that the children jointly receive three-quarters. So each gets

$$\frac{3}{4} \div 2 = \frac{3}{4} \times \frac{1}{2} = \frac{3}{8}$$

If each child gets £6000, this means that

$\frac{3}{8}$ is equivalent to £6000

$\frac{1}{8}$ is equivalent to £2000

$\frac{1}{4}$ is equivalent to £4000 $\left(\text{since } \frac{1}{4} = \frac{2}{8} \right)$

so his wife receives £4000.

Do It Yourself

1 Gary's patio is covered with 10 slabs. In order to make the patio level he has to lift and re-lay 3 of them. What fraction does he lift? What fraction doesn't he lift?

$\frac{3}{10}$ ✓ $\frac{7}{10}$ ✓

2 Say whether each of these pairs of fractions are equivalent:

(i) $\frac{3}{5}$ and $\frac{12}{20}$ (ii) $\frac{4}{12}$ and $\frac{8}{25}$ (iii) $\frac{9}{10}$ and $\frac{99}{100}$

YES ✓   No ✓   No ✓

3 Rewrite each of the following fractions in its lowest form if possible. If this is not possible write 'in lowest form'.

(i) $\frac{4}{8}$ $\frac{1}{2}$ ✓ (ii) $\frac{5}{15}$ $\frac{1}{3}$ ✓ (iii) $\frac{7}{21}$ $\frac{1}{3}$ ✓

(iv) $\frac{3}{16}$ low ✓ (v) $\frac{4}{20}$ $\frac{1}{5}$ ✓ (vi) $\frac{8}{12}$ $\frac{2}{3}$ ✓

4 Identical pies have been cut into quarters. After some have been eaten, there are 27 portions left. How many pies is this? Include any fraction in your answer.

$6\frac{3}{4}$ ✓

5 Change these mixed numbers into improper fractions:

(i) $4\frac{3}{5}$ $\frac{23}{5}$ ✓   (ii) $1\frac{4}{7}$ $\frac{11}{7}$ ✓   (iii) $5\frac{1}{3}$ $\frac{16}{3}$ ✓   (iv) $6\frac{3}{4}$ $\frac{27}{4}$ ✓

For questions 6a, 6b, 7 and 8, make sure that you put the answers in their lowest terms.

6 a Find the result of the following:

(i) $\frac{1}{3}+\frac{2}{5}$ $\frac{11}{15}$ ✓   (ii) $\frac{3}{4}+\frac{5}{8}$ $\frac{11}{8} = 1\frac{3}{8}$ ✓   (iii) $\frac{3}{8}+\frac{2}{9}$ $\frac{27}{72} = \frac{43}{72}$ ✓   (iv) $2\frac{7}{8}+1\frac{1}{4}$ $= 4\frac{1}{8}$ ✓

$\frac{5\ 6}{15}$ $\frac{27}{72}$

b Find the result of the following:

(i) $\frac{2}{3}-\frac{1}{4}$ $= \frac{5}{12}$ ✓   (ii) $\frac{3}{8}-\frac{1}{3}$ $= \frac{1}{24}$ ✓   (iii) $\frac{3}{4}-\frac{3}{5}$ $= \frac{3}{20}$ ✓   (iv) $4\frac{7}{15}-2\frac{2}{3}$ $= 1\frac{4}{5}$ ✓

$8-3$ $9-8$ $15-12$ $\frac{67-8}{}$

$\frac{67-40}{15}$ $\frac{27}{15}$ $1'$

$\frac{12}{15}$

7 Find the result of the following:

(i) $\frac{3}{8}\times\frac{2}{7}$ $= \frac{3}{28}$ ✓   (ii) $\frac{3}{4}\times\frac{4}{5}$ $= \frac{3}{5}$ ✓   (iii) $\frac{4}{9}\times1\frac{1}{3}$ $\frac{16}{27}$ ✓   (iv) $2\frac{3}{4}\times1\frac{2}{3}$ $= 4\frac{7}{12}$ ✓

$\frac{4}{9}\times\frac{4}{3}$ $\frac{11}{4}\times\frac{5}{3} = \frac{55}{12}$

$\frac{16}{27}$

8 Find the result of the following:

(i) $\frac{5}{6}\div\frac{1}{3}$ $\frac{5}{2} = 2\frac{1}{2}$ ✓   (ii) $\frac{5}{7}\div\frac{14}{41}$ $\frac{20}{7} = 2\frac{6}{7}$ ✓   (iii) $1\frac{1}{5}\div\frac{7}{10}$ $= 1\frac{5}{7}$ ✓   (iv) $2\frac{1}{3}\div3\frac{5}{9}$ $= \frac{21}{32}$ ✓

$\frac{6}{5}\times\frac{10}{7} = \frac{12}{7} = 1$ $\frac{7}{3}\times\frac{9^3}{32} = \frac{21}{32}$

$\frac{21}{32}$

9 In a sponsored walk Julia walked $\frac{3}{4}$ of the maximum distance allowed. Sally walked 16 miles, or $\frac{4}{5}$ of the maximum distance allowed.

(i) What is the maximum distance allowed?   20 miles ✓
(ii) How far did Julia walk?   15 miles ✓

4 Decimals, Percentages and Ratios

Things You Need to Know

1 Decimals are a form of fraction based upon using 10, or 100, or 1000, or 10 000 and so on:

$$\frac{1}{10} = 0.1 \qquad \frac{1}{100} = 0.01 \qquad \frac{1}{1000} = 0.001$$

so

$$\frac{9}{10} = 0.9 \qquad \frac{57}{100} = 0.57 \qquad \frac{367}{1000} = 0.367$$

2 Changing a decimal to a fraction is simply a matter of putting the correct denominator under the figures:

$$0.3 = \frac{3}{10} \qquad 0.09 = \frac{9}{100} \qquad 0.25 = \frac{25}{100} = \frac{1}{4} \qquad 2.3 = \frac{23}{10} = 2\frac{3}{10}$$

Notice that here the number of zeros in the denominator is the same as the number of figures to the right of the decimal point.

3 To put numbers into order, first of all use the whole number part then use each figure after the decimal point in turn:

8.79	4.23	4.29	6.874	4.78

Using the whole number first, these become

8.79	6.874	4.23	4.29	4.78

Where the whole numbers are the same, using the first decimal place gives

8.79	6.874	4.78	4.23	4.29

Where the whole number and the first decimal place are equal, using the second decimal place gives

8.79	6.874	4.78	4.29	4.23

In this example we have finished but if we had to continue we would move to the third decimal place, then the fourth, and so on . . .

4 The word **percentage** means 'out of 100'. The symbol used for it is %, so 8% means 8 parts out of 100 parts.

5 One of the main uses of percentages is for comparing things, like test marks – especially when the test marks are 'out of' different possible maximums.

6 Converting from a percentage to a fraction is just a matter of writing the fraction with 100 as the denominator and the percentage figure as the numerator. For example, 40% is $\frac{40}{100}$, which cancels to give $\frac{2}{5}$.

7 Converting from a percentage to a decimal means dividing the percentage figure by 100. For example, 37% = 0.37.

8 Converting a fraction to a percentage means multiplying the fraction by 100 (in other words, what part of 100 is the fraction?). For example, $\frac{7}{25}$ is $\frac{700}{25}$% which simplified becomes 28%.

9 Converting from a decimal to a percentage also means multiplying by 100. For example, 0.31 is 31%.

10 Decimals are used a great deal when making an 'intelligent guess', known in maths as **trial and improvement**. When we do this we try to refine our guess and keep on making it better until it is accurate enough for what is wanted. For example, to find the square root of 3, we know it is between 1 and 2 ($1^2 = 1$ and $2^2 = 4$), so we could start with 1.5.

$1.5^2 = 2.25$	so 1.5 is too small
$1.7^2 = 2.89$	still too small
$1.8^2 = 3.24$	too large

So the square root of 3 is between 1.7 and 1.8.

$1.75^2 = 3.0625$	too large
$1.73^2 = 2.9929$	close, but too small
$1.735^2 = 3.010225$	too large
$1.732^2 = 2.999824$	very close, but too small
$1.7325^2 = 3.0015563$	again very close, but too large
$1.7321^2 = 3.0001704$	very, very close, but too large
$1.73205^2 = 2.9999972$	very, very, very close but too small

We could continue with this until we had the square root of 3 as accurate as is wanted. From the above we know it is between 1.73205 and 1.7321. So correct to 4 decimal places the answer is 1.7321.

11 **Ratio** is a way of comparing objects. Ratios are very similar to fractions in many ways. For example, if one object is twice the size of another, then the ratio of their sizes is $1:2$. In other words, the first object is $\frac{1}{2}$ of the second, or the second object is twice the size of the first.

As with fractions, we always try to write a ratio in its simplest form. So, if there are 250 boys and 300 girls in a school, the ratio of boys to girls is $250:300$. Since they can both be divided by 50, this becomes $5:6$. In other words, for every 5 boys there are 6 girls.

How to Do It

1 Write each of the following as fractions:

    (i) 0.45   (ii) 0.07   (iii) 0.109

Solution

(i) $0.45 = \frac{45}{100} = \frac{9}{20}$ (ii) $0.07 = \frac{7}{100}$ (iii) $0.109 = \frac{109}{1000}$

2 Convert the following decimals to fractions, writing the answer in its simplest form:

    (i) 0.75   (ii) 0.6   (iii) 0.375

Solution

(i) $0.75 = \frac{75}{100}$ (now divide numerator and denominator by 5)

       $= \frac{15}{20}$ (now divide them by 5 again)

       $= \frac{3}{4}$

(ii) $0.6 = \frac{6}{10}$

     $= \frac{3}{5}$

(iii) $0.375 = \frac{375}{1000}$ (now divide numerator and denominator by 5)

         $= \frac{75}{200}$ (now divide them by 5 again)

         $= \frac{15}{40}$ (now divide them by 5 again)

         $= \frac{3}{8}$

3 On the number line below indicate the position of each of the following numbers: 3.65 2.85 5.27 4.65 4.32 1.75

Solution

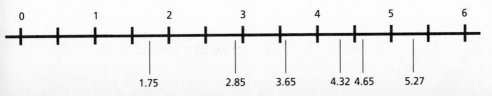

4 Helen scored 66 marks in an examination. What would be her mark as a percentage if the examination had a maximum of:

(i) 100 marks (ii) 150 marks

Solution

(i) Since Helen got 66 out of a maximum of 100, her mark is 66%.

(ii) 66 out of 150 $= \frac{66}{150} \times 100\%$

$= 44\%$

5 If Peter scored 7 out of 10 in a test and Jane scored 18 out of 25 in a different test, who got the better percentage mark?

Solution

Peter: 7 out of 10 is 70%

Jane: 18 out of 25 $= \frac{18}{25} \times 100\%$

$= 72\%$

So Jane got 2% better marks than Peter.

6 What is 65% as a fraction?

Solution

$65\% = \frac{65}{100}$ (now divide by 5)

$= \frac{13}{20}$

7 What is 71% as a decimal?

Solution

$71\% = \frac{71}{100}$

$= 0.71$

8 What is $\frac{2}{5}$ as a percentage?

Solution

$$\frac{2}{5} = \frac{2}{5} \times 100\%$$
$$= \frac{200}{5}\%$$
$$= 40\%$$

9 What is 0.645 as a percentage figure?

Solution

$$0.645 = 0.645 \times 100\%$$
$$= 64.5\%$$
$$\text{or} = 64\tfrac{1}{2}\%$$

10 The divide button on your calculator has stopped working; however, the multiply button continues to work satisfactorily. Find $19 \div 4.25$ to 4 decimal places (d.p.).

Solution

$19 \div 4.25$ is probably between 4 and 5, so let's try 4.5.

$4.5 \times 4.25 = 19.125$	so 4.5 is too big
$4.4 \times 4.25 = 18.7$	too small
$4.45 \times 4.25 = 18.9125$	too small
$4.47 \times 4.25 = 18.9975$	still too small
$4.48 \times 4.25 = 19.04$	too big

So it is between 4.48 and 4.47.

$4.475 \times 4.25 = 19.01875$	too big
$4.471 \times 4.25 = 19.001$	too big

So it is between 4.47 and 4.471.

$4.4705 \times 4.25 = 18.999625$	too small
$4.4706 \times 4.25 = 19.00005$	too big
$4.47055 \times 4.25 = 18.999838$	too small

So it is between 4.47055 and 4.4706.

Thus, $19 \div 4.25 = 4.4706$ corr to 4 d.p.

11 **a** A man is 32 years old and his daughter is 8 years old. What is the ratio o the man's age to the daughter's age?

Solution

The ratio is $32:8$

which simplifies to $4:1$

b An alloy consists of copper and tin in the ratio $7:3$. How much copper i needed if I have 12 kg of tin?

copper : tin is $7:3$

This has to be the same as copper : 12

So, because the 3 was multiplied by 4 to become 12,

the weight of copper $= 4 \times 7$
$= 28\,kg$

Do It Yourself

1 Change the following fractions into decimals:

(i) $\dfrac{63}{100}$ (ii) $\dfrac{7}{10}$ (iii) $\dfrac{745}{1000}$

(iv) $\dfrac{3}{100}$ (v) $\dfrac{12}{1000}$

2 Convert each of the following decimals into fractions in their simplest forn

(i) 0.75   (ii) 0.31   (iii) 0.05

(iv) 0.33   (v) 0.125

3 The times for six runners in a race are:

No. 1   10.83 sec.   No. 4   10.76 sec.
No. 2   11.05 sec.   No. 5   11.30 sec.
No. 3   10.35 sec.   No. 6   10.91 sec.

(i) What is the number of the runner who came first?
(ii) What is the number of the runner who came third?
(iii) What is the number of the runner who came last?

a The petrol tank of Ali's car holds 50 litres of petrol when full and the car uses 1 litre of petrol for every 15 km travelled. If his tank was 80% full, how far can he travel before he runs out of petrol?

b Find:

     (i) 25% of £5.00;

     (ii) $12\frac{1}{2}$% of £4.96;

     (iii) 30% of 8 m.

c In a sale the marked prices are reduced by 15%. How much would Mary have to pay for a pair of jeans marked at £37.00?

d VAT (see page 40) is currently charged at $17\frac{1}{2}$%. Find the full price of each of the following goods:

     (i) sofa bed   £199 + VAT;

     (ii) CD player   £92.50 + VAT;

     (iii) cricket bat £32.00 + VAT.

5 Alline scores 39 marks out of a possible 60 in an examination. What is her percentage mark? What grade would she be awarded if the lowest marks for the grades are:

Grade A lowest mark   70%

Grade B lowest mark   60%

Grade C lowest mark   45%

Fail if less than 45%

6 Convert the following percentages into fractions in the lowest terms:

    (i) 25%   (ii) 30%   (iii) 45%   (iv) $33\frac{1}{3}$%   (v) 125%

7 Convert the following percentages into decimals:

    (i) 25%   (ii) 43%   (iii) 50%

    (iv) 80%   (v) 120%   (vi) 275%

8 **a** In a science test Rashid scored 16 out of 20. What percentage is this?

b Paula paid a deposit of £7.20 for a Walkman. The cash price for the Walkman is £72.00. What percentage of the cash price is the deposit?

9 Convert each of the following decimals into percentages:

(i) 0.5 (ii) 0.75 (iii) 0.16 (iv) 0.35 (v) 1.74

10 By trial and improvement, find the cube root of 12 to two decimal places. (Hint: since $2^3 = 8$ and $3^3 = 27$ it is between 2 and 3. As 12 is nearer to 8 than 27, start off with 2.3.)

11 **a** (i) Divide £48.00 in the ratio 1 : 3.
(ii) Divide 28 m in the ratio 4 : 3.
(iii) Divide 65 kg in the ratio 6 : 5 : 2.

b The ratio of the length of a room to its width is 6 : 5. If the room is 7.2 m long, how wide is it?

Practical Maths

hings You Need to Know

People are often paid by the number of hours they work. For example, Sally works 30 hours at £4.50 per hour so Sally earns

$$30 \times £4.50 = £135.00$$

Overtime payment arises when someone works above a certain number of hours. For these extra hours they will often be paid at a different rate (e.g. 'time and a half' − meaning $1\frac{1}{2}$ times the normal rate) to compensate for the longer hours. For example, if Diana worked 35 hours and 5 hours' overtime at time and a quarter, and if her normal rate is £3.00, she gets

$$35 \times £3.00 + 1\tfrac{1}{4} \times 5 \times £3.00 = £105.00 + 18.75$$
$$= £123.75$$

CONTENTS

2 The Government takes some of our money as **income tax** to help pay for things like the health and education services. This tax is usually a percentage of what you have earned above a certain amount (called a **personal allowance**). For example, if Diana earns £123.75 in a week and has a weekly personal allowance of £33.75, and if she is taxed at 25% she pays tax on

$$£123.75 - £33.75 = £90.00$$

The tax she pays is

$$25\% \times £90.00 = £22.50$$

BODGETT & SON
P L U M B E R S

INV NO 234

Call-out charge	£15.00
½ hours work @ £18.00 per hour	9.00
Materials	2.50
Sub total	£26.50
VAT at 17½%	4.64
Total	£31.14

3 **Bills** are what we pay whenever we have any work done. We might employ a plumber to mend a leak in a water pipe and his bill might look something like the one shown here.

VAT, or value added tax, is added to the amount he charges. This is a tax put on the price of some goods, which is then paid to the government. It is calculated as a percentage of the price. (Currently, the percentage rate is $17\frac{1}{2}\%$.)

4 You have to pay to borrow money; this is called **interest**. The amount depends upon how much you borrow, the percentage rate of the interest and the length of time you borrow the money for.

With **simple interest** the interest is calculated on the amount and the number of years – the rate is expressed as so much 'per annum' (or year). For example, if you borrow £200.00 for 2 years at 6% per annum interest, the interest is

$$6\% \times £200 \times 2 = £24.00$$

So you'll have to pay back a total of £224.00 – the original £200.00 plus the £24.00 interest.

Compound interest is interest charged at regular intervals on the amount owing at that time, with the interest being added to the amount owed. This new figure is then used the next time the interest is calculated.

Hire purchase is a way of buying goods by paying a small amount of money regularly (say, monthly) over a period of time – often an initial deposit is required when you start. The final total paid is usually more than if you had paid cash when you bought the goods.

'The rate of interest is the percentage of the initial loan you are charged for every year'

How to Do It

Fred works as a waiter. His basic wage is £2.40 an hour. If he works after 10.00 p.m. he gets paid time and a half. Here is his time sheet for Saturday. Fill in the gaps:

Lunchtime			Evening				Total Time	
On	Off	Hours	on	off	Hours		Basic	O/T
					Basic	O/T		
10.00	2.30		7.00	11.15				

.... hours' basic @ £2.40 per hour ....

.... hours' overtime @ .... per hour ....

Total earned = ...

Solution

Lunchtime			Evening				Total Time	
On	Off	Hours	on	off	Hours		Basic	O/T
					Basic	O/T		
10.00	2.30	4½	7.00	11.15	3	1¼	7½	1¼

7½ hours' basic @ £2.40 per hour 18.00

1¼ hours' overtime @ £3.60 per hour 4.50

Total earned = £22.50

41

2 Jane Vicars has a tax-free allowance of £4000 per annum and her income is £21 300 per annum. If she pays tax at the rate of 25% how much tax does she pay in a year?

Solution

Jane's taxable income is

$$£21\,300 - £4000 = £17\,300$$

Tax paid is

$$25\% \times £17\,300 = £4325$$

ROCKY'S TV REPAIRS

£14.00 call-out fee
£12.00 per hour labour
plus parts
plus VAT

Phone 098765 4321 for service

3 Joe's television needs repairing. He calls out an engineer from Rocky's. The engineer is at the house for $1\frac{1}{4}$ hours, and replaces a circuit board costing £23.45 and a fuse costing 40p. VAT is charged at $17\frac{1}{2}\%$.

(i) How much is charged for labour?
(ii) How much is charged for parts?
(iii) How much is the total bill before tax?
(iv) How much is the VAT?
(v) What is the final amount to pay?

Solution

(i) Labour charge is

$$1\tfrac{1}{4} \times £12.00 = £15.00$$

(ii) Parts cost

$$£23.45 + 40p = £23.85$$

(iii) Total bill before VAT is call-out fee + labour charge + parts cost, or

$$£14.00 + £15.00 + £23.85 = £52.85$$

(iv) VAT is

$$17\tfrac{1}{2}\% \times £52.85 = £9.25 \quad \text{(to the nearest penny)}$$

(v) Final bill is

$$£52.85 + £9.25 = £62.10$$

4 At the beginning of the year Jean had £3175.64 in her building society account. She did not pay anything into the account or withdraw anything for a year. At the end of the year she had £3344.42 in the account. How much interest had she been paid by the building society?

Solution

Interest is

$$£3344.42 - £3175.64 = £168.78$$

5 Granny invests her savings of £27 500 at 7% interest per annum. At the end of each year she takes the interest to use; how much interest does she get?

Solution

Each year she gets

$$7\% \times £27\,500 = £1925$$

6 If Granny in question 5 had left the interest in the account how much would she have after 3 years?

Solution

Year 1:

$$\text{The amount of money at the start of year 1} = £27\,500$$
$$\text{The interest earned} = 7\% \times £27\,500$$
$$= £1925$$
$$\text{So the amount at the end of year 1} = £29\,425$$

Year 2:

$$\text{The amount of money at the start of year 2} = £29\,425$$
$$\text{The interest earned} = 7\% \times £29\,425$$
$$= £2059.75$$
$$\text{So the amount at the end of year 2} = £31\,484.75$$

Year 3:

The amount of money at the start of year 3 = £31 484.75
The interest earned = 7% × £31 484.75
= £2203.93
So the amount at the end of year 3 = £33 688.68

(Note how the interest each year is getting larger – because the previous year's interest is gaining interest. We have assumed that the interest rate stays the same – this is not always so in real life!)

7 Derek decides to buy a car. The car he would like has a cash price of £7995. However, he could pay a deposit of £199 and pay 48 monthly payments of £199. How much extra does he pay if he decides to buy the car using the hire purchase scheme?

Total of the payments = 48 × £199
= £9552
Deposit = £199
So total paid = £9751
The extra he has to pay = £9751 − £7995
= £1756

Do It Yourself

1 a Jenny is paid £3.75 an hour. She works from 9.00a.m. until 5.30p.m. each day from Monday to Friday, with an hour for lunch. How much does she earn in a week?

b Your uncle offers you a part-time job helping with his decorating business. He will pay you £1.75 an hour and double time on Sunday. You work from 9.00 a.m. until 4.00 p.m. on Saturday, with a 1-hour break for lunch and a break of 30 minutes for tea. In order to finish the job, you do 3 hours on Sunday morning.
  (i) How many hours do you work at the basic rate?
  (ii) How much basic pay do you get?
  (iii) How many hours' overtime do you work?
  (iv) What is your overtime pay?
  (v) How much does your uncle give you for the weekend's work?

2 Rashid earns £1250 a month. He is taxed at the rate of 25p in the pound. However, he has a yearly personal allowance of £2400. How much tax does Rashid pay in a year?

3 Mr Smith's car repair bill is £113.50, not including VAT. If VAT is charged at $17\frac{1}{2}\%$, what is the final total for his bill?

4 Jane borrowed £600 to buy a hi-fi. Having paid a deposit of £100, she paid the loan back with 10 equal payments of £55. How much interest did she pay?

5 Anne put £100 into her savings account each year for 4 years, and each year the rate of interest was 6% p.a. At the end of each year she withdrew all the interest paid. How much interest has Anne received over the 4 years?

6 Brian invested £400 in a savings account, where it earned him 6% per annum interest. At the end of each year he withdrew £100, but left the interest in the account. After 4 years he withdrew all the money. How much interest had he earned over the 4 years?

7 Instead of paying the cash price of £480 for a television, a family decides to buy it by hire purchase. There are two schemes available for them:

   Scheme A: deposit of £80 and 6 monthly payments of £75
   Scheme B: deposit of £100 and 10 monthly payments of £45

Which scheme charges less interest and by how much?

6 | Scale, Maps and Bearings

Things You Need to Know

1 A **scale** tells you how the model/drawing compares to the real thing. It is usually written like:

1:15   or 1 to 15   or $\frac{1}{15}$ or 1 cm represents 15 cm

(All of these mean the same – that 1 unit on the model corresponds to 15 units on the real thing.)

2 A **scale drawing** is a drawing in which all the lengths of the lines are to scale. Only the lengths of the sides are to scale – *not the angles*, otherwise a large square drawn to scale would not look like a square!

drawn to a scale of
1 : 4

3 **Bearings** are used with maps. A bearing is usually given as the angle you would have to turn through if you started by facing north and turned clockwise until you were facing in the direction you wanted. Bearings are always given as three figures, so an angle of 75°, for example, is written as 075°.

In the diagram above, P is on a bearing of 075° from T, and S is on a bearing of 120° from T. If you were at S and wanted to get to T, this would be as shown in the diagram on the right:

We can work out that angle S is 300° (see top of page 78). Hence T is on a bearing of 300° from S.

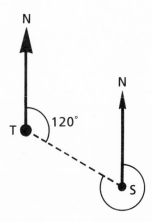

(see top of page 78)

'A bearing is a way of giving a direction'

4 The scale on a map is used in exactly the same way as any other scale – it is just that usually the scale is so much smaller. An Ordnance Survey map of an area may have a scale:

1 : 50 000   (this might be given as 2 cm to 1 km)

Like any other scale, it is used when calculating distances.

How to Do It

'Scale is the ratio of the length on a model to the length on the real thing'

1 Geoff has built himself a model of the Jaguar 'E-type'. It is to a scale of 1 : 32.

(i) On the box it says that the length of the model is 139 mm. What is the length of the real car?

(ii) If the width of the real car is 1.66 m, how wide is the model car (to the nearest millimetre)?

Solution

(i) 1 mm on the model is 32 mm on the real car so

$$139 \text{ mm on the model} = 139 \times 32 \text{ mm on the real car}$$
$$= 4448 \text{ mm}$$
$$= 4.448 \text{ m}$$

(ii) 1 mm on the model is 32 mm on the real car so $\frac{1}{32}$ mm on the model is 1 mm on the real car. Hence

$$\tfrac{1}{32} \times 1660 \text{ mm on the model} = 1.66 \text{ m} = 1660 \text{ mm on the real car}$$
$$\text{so the width of the model} = 1660 \text{ mm} \div 32 = 52 \text{ mm} \quad \text{(to the nearest mm)}$$

2 The diagram shows part of a plan for a car park. The scale is 1 : 200. What is the width allowed for a car? What is the length allowed for a car?

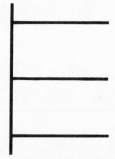

Solution

Measuring from the plan, the width is 14 mm and the length is 26 mm. The width allowed in the car park is

$$200 \times 14 \text{ mm} = 2800 \text{ mm}$$
$$= 2.80 \text{ m}$$

The length allowed is

$$200 \times 26 \text{ mm} = 5200 \text{ mm}$$
$$= 5.20 \text{ m}$$

3 On the map, what is the bearing of There from Here?

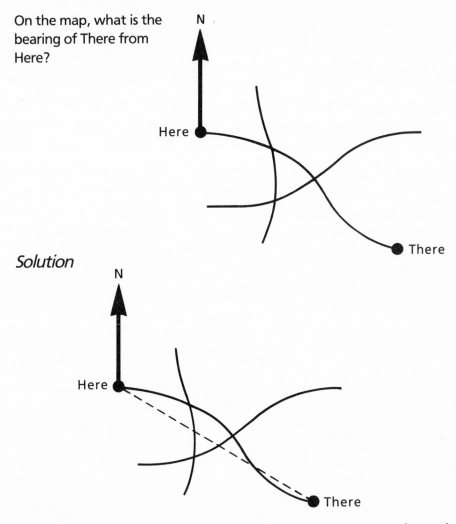

Solution

By drawing a straight line from Here to There we can measure the angle between it and the north line; it is 117°. So the bearing of There from Here is 117°.

4 On the map in question 3, how far is it (as the crow flies) from Here to There? The scale is 1 : 50 000.

Solution

The distance measured on the map is 5.1 cm (or 51 mm). So the actual distance is

$$50\,000 \times 5.1\,\text{cm} = 2550\,\text{m}$$
$$= 2.55\,\text{km}$$

Do It Yourself

1 The plan of a house has a scale of 1 : 100.
   (i) What length, in metres, does 1 cm on the plan represent?
   (ii) If the dining room on the plan has dimensions 5 cm by 4 cm, what will the actual size of the dining room be?
   (iii) The smallest bedroom measures 3.5 m by 2.5 m. What size is it on the plan?

2a A map of the Isle of Wight has a scale of 1 : 25 000.
   (i) What distance, in metres, does 1 cm on the map represent?
   (ii) The distance between two telephone boxes is 12 cm on the map. How far apart in kilometres are they?
   (iii) Two villages are 4 km apart. How far apart are they on the map?

'When doing a scale drawing, always use a sharp pencil and don't forget to give the scale '

b Here is a rough sketch showing the distances between three villages A, B and C. Use a scale of 1 cm : 1 km to draw it accurately.

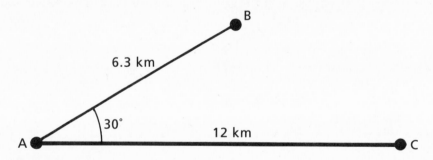

How far apart are B and C (correct to one decimal place)?

3 Isobel lives 200 m due east of George, and Phil lives 45 m due south of George. Make a scale drawing with a scale of 1 cm to represent 10 m. Using your scale drawing find:
   (i) the distance from Isobel's to Phil's house;
   (ii) the bearing of Phil's house from Isobel's house.

4 Sarah and Katy are 4 km apart. On a map they are 16 cm apart. What is the scale of the map?

Mass, Length and Capacity

Things You Need to Know

We measure mass, or weight, in **grams** in the metric system. There are other units based on the gram:

$$1 \text{ gram (g)} = 1000 \text{ milligrams (mg)}$$
$$1 \text{ kilogram (kg)} = 1000 \text{ g}$$
$$1 \text{ tonne (t)} = 1000 \text{ kg}$$

In everyday life, mass and weight are used to mean the same thing, but in science they are different.

Length is measured using the **metre**. Again there are other units based on the metre:

$$1 \text{ centimetre (cm)} = 10 \text{ millimetres (mm)}$$
$$1 \text{ metre} = 100 \text{ cm} \quad (\text{or } 1 \text{ m} = 1000 \text{ mm})$$
$$1 \text{ kilometre (km)} = 1000 \text{ m}$$

The basic unit of capacity is the **litre**:

$$1 \text{ centilitre (cl)} = 10 \text{ millilitres (ml)}$$
$$1 \text{ litre (l)} = 100 \text{ cl} \quad (\text{or } 1 \text{ litre} = 1000 \text{ ml})$$

4 Sometimes we need to approximate between the metric and imperial systems:

> 1 kg is slightly more than 2 pounds   (2 lbs)
> 8 km is about 5 miles
> 30 cm is about 1 foot
> 1 litre is about $1\frac{3}{4}$ pints   (in other words a little under 2 pints).

How to Do It

1 Convert 0.3 tonnes to kilograms.

Solution

> 1 tonne $= 1000\,kg$
> 0.3 tonne $= 0.3 \times 1000\,kg$
> $= 300\,kg$

2 Convert 6370 m to kilometres.

Solution

> $1000\,m = 1\,km$
> $1\,m = \frac{1}{1000}\,km$
> $6370\,m = 6370 \times \frac{1}{1000}\,km$
> $= \frac{6370}{1000}\,km$
> $= 6.37\,km$

'Be careful: there is the tonne (metric) and the ton (imperial) – they sound the same but they aren't quite (1 ton = 1.02 tonnes)'

3 Convert 0.35 litres to millilitres.

Solution

> 1 litre $= 1000\,ml$
> 0.35 litres $= 0.35 \times 1000\,ml$
> $= 350\,ml$

What is a speed of 30 miles/hour in kilometres/hour? (Use 5 miles as approximately 8 km.)

Solution

$$5 \text{ miles} = 8 \text{ km}$$
$$1 \text{ mile} = \tfrac{8}{5} \text{ km}$$
$$30 \text{ miles} = 30 \times \tfrac{8}{5} \text{ km}$$
$$= \tfrac{240}{5} \text{ km}$$
$$= 48 \text{ km}$$

So 30 miles/hour = 48 km/hr.

Do It Yourself

a Convert the following weights to kilograms:

    (i) 7431 g   (ii) 376 100 mg   (iii) 2.5 t

b A security guard delivers £100 in 1p pieces to a supermarket. If a 1p coin weighs 3.45 g, calculate the weight of the coins in kilograms.

c Arrange the following weights in order of size, smallest first:

    70 g   0.7 kg   700 mg   0.07 g

a Convert the following to millimetres:

    (i) 4.6 cm   (ii) 7.9 cm   (iii) 9.1 m   (iv) 31.2 cm

b Convert the following to centimetres:

    (i) 5 m   (ii) 9.2 m   (iii) 740 mm   (iv) 6431 mm

c Convert the following to kilometres:

    (i) 8000 m   (ii) 400 m   (iii) 21 m

'The metric system is simply based around dividing and multiplying by tens'

3 **a** Convert the following to litres:

   (i) 500 ml   (ii) 6000 ml

   b Convert the following to millilitres:

   (i) 5.2 litres   (ii) 0.75 litres

'Use a calculator only if really needed – but remember you are only converting approxi- mately, so don't use any conversion buttons on the calculator'

4 Convert each of these measurements approximately into the units given:
   (i) 70 kg in lbs   (ii) 40 km in miles   (iii) 8 litres in pints
   (iv) 26 lbs in kg   (v) 35 miles in km   (vi) 21 pints in litres

Reminder:
1 kg is a little under 2 lbs
8 km is about 5 miles
1 litre is about $1\frac{3}{4}$ pints
    or a little under 2 pints

Probability

Things You Need to Know

Some things in life are certain – for example, $3 \times 4 = 12$ is always true.
Some things in life are impossible (e.g. it is impossible to jump to the
Moon). It is also true that some things may or may not happen (such as the
horse you select winning the race). Probability attempts to measure how
likely something is to happen (like your football team winning on
Saturday). A scale going from 0 to 1 is used to express probability:

0   1

**Will definitely
not happen**   **Will definitely
happen**

One way to find the probability of an event happening is to see how many
times it occurs out of a lot of trials. For example, a drawing pin is thrown in
the air and can land point up or point down. If it is thrown 200 times and
lands with the point up 80 times, we deduce that the probability of the
drawing pin landing point up is $\frac{80}{200}$; this cancels to $\frac{2}{5}$ (you might even write
it as 0.4).

3 Some things are a little more predictable in that we know we are going to get the same number for each of the possible occurrences in the long run. For example, with a dice we know that there are six possible occurrences and each can happen equally often – so the probability of getting a 2, say, is $\frac{1}{6}$, as $\frac{1}{6}$ of the time (in the long run) we will get a 2.

$$\text{Probability of event} = \frac{\text{number of ways event can happen}}{\text{total number of possible outcomes}}$$

4 Some probabilities for dice, cards and coins:

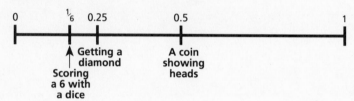

How to Do It

1 During the summer holidays Anna will be going out 15 times with her favourite aunt. If the probability of her aunt buying her an ice-cream (from past experience) is $\frac{3}{5}$, how many times is Anna likely to get an ice-cream?

Solution

$$\text{Number of times} = \frac{3}{5} \times 15 = 9 \text{ times}$$

2 Sally threw a dart at a dartboard trying to score a treble 20. Out of 150 throws at the treble 20, she got it 90 times. What is the probability of Sally throwing a treble 20?

Solution
Probability of Sally throwing a treble 20 is

$$\frac{90}{150} = \frac{9}{15}$$

$$= \frac{3}{5} \quad \text{or} \quad 0.6$$

3 In a bag are some bars of chocolate all the same size. The bag contains:

8 bars of milk chocolate

6 bars of white chocolate

6 bars of plain chocolate

If I dip into the bag and take a bar of chocolate at random, what is the probability of its being white chocolate?

Solution

Number of ways the event can happen $= 6$ (number of bars of white chocolate)

Number of possible outcomes $= 8 + 6 + 6$ (total number of bars)

   $= 20$

So probability of a white bar being randomly selected $= \frac{6}{20}$

   $= \frac{3}{10}$ (or 0.3)

4 On the following probability scale, mark the probability of drawing a picture card (king, queen or jack) from a pack of cards.

Solution

Number of picture cards in a pack is

$3 \times 4 = 12$ (3 cards in each of 4 suits)

There are 52 cards in a pack so the probability of drawing a picture card is

$\frac{12}{52} = \frac{3}{13}$ (or 0.23 . . .)

so it would appear on the scale as follows:

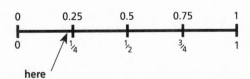

here

Do It Yourself

1 Here is a probability scale with some probability values marked as a, b, c and d. Write down the meaning of each of the probabilities marked. (The first has been done for you.)

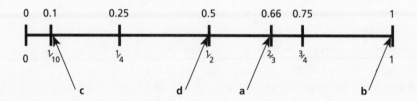

(a) This means that the event will occur approximately $\frac{2}{3}$ of the time in the long run; in other words, out of, say, 3000 times the event will occur about 2000 times.

2 Diana is taking pencils out of a large container of pencils. She takes 50 out at random, but of the 50 pencils 15 are broken. What is the probability of taking out a broken pencil from this container?

3a The letters of the word 'mathematics' are each put on to a card. The cards are mixed and one is taken. What is the probability of the card having:
(i) the letter 'm' on it   (ii) a vowel on it

b Copy and complete this table, showing the sums which can be obtained by taking one number from each of the following sets of numbers:

$$\{1, 3, 5, 7\}$$
$$\text{and} \quad \{2, 4, 6, 8\}$$

	1	3	5	7
2	3	5		
4				
6				
8				15

If Gemma picks a number from the first set and Ian picks a number from the second set, what is the probability that the sum of the two numbers is:

(i) 9 (ii) greater than 9 (iii) odd (iv) a multiple of 3

4 Find the probability of each of the following four events occurring, and mark their places on a copy of the probability scale.

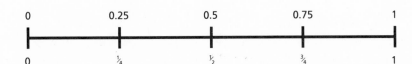

(i) The probability of drawing a red card from a normal pack of 52 playing cards

(ii) The probability of selecting a boy from a class of 30 pupils, 12 of whom are girls

(iii) The probability of drawing a red sock from a drawer that contains only black socks

(iv) The probability of picking the letter 'f' from the word 'flagstaff'.

59

9

Tables, Graphs, Pie Charts and Averages

Things You Need to Know

1   A **graph** is a way of showing how two sets of data are connected. It has two axes at right angles to each other – with the *x*-axis going across (*x* – a cross!) and the *y*-axis going vertically.

2   A point on a graph has a pair of **coordinates** telling how far across the point is and how far up it is. For example, the point (3, 5) is shown on the graph at the right.

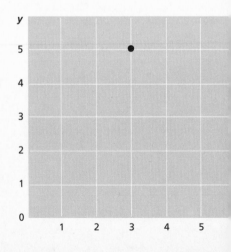

3 When a set of points has been plotted, they may be in a straight line (in which case use a ruler to join them up). Information such as temperature readings, for example, is joined from point to point with a series of straight lines. Or they may be on a fairly smooth curve (try to join them up smoothly, turning the paper round if it helps), or there may not be any real line you can draw through them (in which case leave them as points).

4 **Tally tables** are useful as a way of collecting information together (and counting it easily). They tell you how many times something has occurred. As you mark each tally put a | and when you get to the fifth put a line through the other four. For example:

Means 12

5 The number of times something has happened is called the frequency. The frequency is plotted on **frequency charts**, or **bar charts**, like the one shown below. (The bars may touch each other, but they do not have to.)

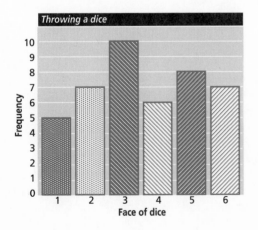

'Always write the x-value first – remember x comes before y in the alphabet'

'Remember, there are 360° in a full circle'

6 **Pie charts** are another way of presenting information. They are used when we want to compare a part with the whole. For example, 24 children gave their favourite sport:

8 said soccer

4 said rugby

5 said cricket

7 said tennis

This gives the pie chart here.

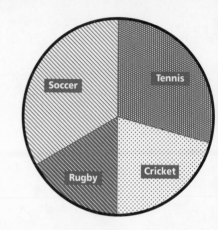

'Note the value of 20 litres = 35 pints is used here'

7 One use of graphs is to convert from one system to another. For example, 1 litre = 1.75 pints gives the graph shown on the right. Note that we have used 20 litres = 35 pints to draw the graph.

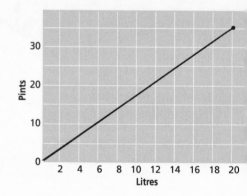

8 The word 'average' simply means 'a central value'. If all the measurements in a set have to be represented by a single number, what should that number be? There are three main contenders.

  (i) **Mean** – usually what people understand when they say 'average':

$$\text{Mean} = \frac{\text{sum of all the values}}{\text{number of values}}$$

   (Note that it can only be used with number information.)

 (ii) **Mode** – this is the most popular value in the data – the one that occurs most often. It is often used for data which do not have a numerical value (like the sport example in no. 6).

(iii) **Median** – this is the middle value when all the values are arranged in order. If there is not a single value in the middle, we take the value midway between the two middle values.

ow to Do It

On a piece of graph paper draw the x-axis and the y-axis going from 0 to 8. Plot every point whose x-value is one more than its y-value.

If $y = 0$ $x = 1$
If $y = 1$ $x = 2$

and so on.

Solution

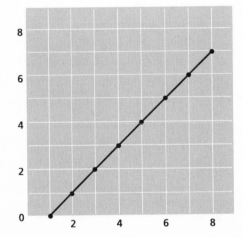

> *'When the graph is a straight line, we don't need more than three points (the third one provides a check)'*

Draw the graph of $y = x^2 - 1$, with the values of x ranging from -1 to $+3$.

Solution

The (x, y) values have to be worked out in a table:

x	-1	0	1	3	3
x^2	1	0	1	4	9
$y = x^2 - 1$	0	-1	0	3	8

From the table it is clear that the y-values vary from -1 to 8, so the y-axis must cover this range. The graph is shown overleaf.

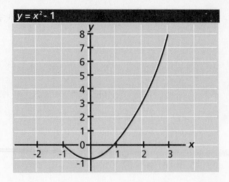

3 Here are the number of goals scored by a school hockey team for the last 10 matches:

Match	1	2	3	4	5	6	7	8	9	10
Goals	1	0	3	1	2	2	4	1	3	0

Plot these values on squared paper. Does it make sense to join them up with a series of straight lines?

Solution

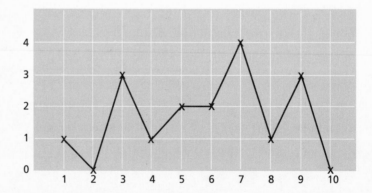

They *can* be joined up with straight lines, as shown here, but it does not give any extra information – it simply makes it easier to look at.

Terry threw a dice 60 times. Here are the results:

```
5  5  6  1  6  4  1  3  6  4
4  2  4  4  3  3  2  2  5  3
3  3  3  5  5  2  6  5  1  6
6  6  1  5  3  1  5  2  4  6
5  2  3  6  3  2  2  2  6  1
5  4  5  6  5  1  1  3  6  1
```

Using a tally table, find the frequency of each possible throw.

Solution

Result	Tally	Frequency
1	ЖЖ IIII	9
2	ЖЖ IIII	9
3	ЖЖ ЖЖ I	11
4	ЖЖ II	7
5	ЖЖ ЖЖ II	12
6	ЖЖ ЖЖ II	12
Total		60

For the frequency table in question 4, draw a frequency (bar) chart to illustrate the results.

Solution
The frequency chart is shown on the right.

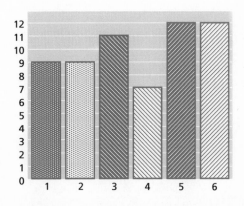

'Always check the total of the frequency – it should be the same as the overall number of values. It is usually a good idea to check one of the values/ frequencies'

6 Thirty-six people were asked their reasons for shopping at a particular supermarket. The results were:

'It is near'	8 people
'Low prices'	9 people
'Have items I like'	12 people
'A special offer'	4 people
'Other reasons'	3 people

Draw a pie chart to illustrate these data.

Reason	Number	Angle
'It is near'	8	80°
'Low prices'	9	90°
'Have items I like'	12	120°
'A special offer'	4	40°
'Other reasons'	3	30°

Solution

As there are 36 people and the circle has 360°, each person must take up 10°, so the angles shown in the chart on the left can be calculated for the data.

Using these angles, we can draw the pie chart:

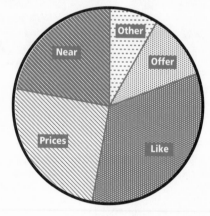

'Graphs and charts can tell us things quicker than if the information is written down'

7 The graph on the right converts between British money (£) and German money (DM) at the rate of 3DM to £1. Use this graph to work out:
  (i) how many DM is £7
  (ii) how many £ you get for 36DM

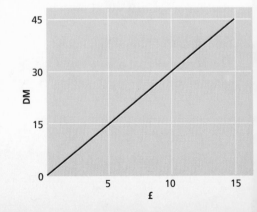

Solution

(i) From £7 on the £ axis (horizontal) go up to the graph line and then across to the DM scale. £7 is worth 21DM.

(ii) From 36DM on the DM axis go along to the graph line then down to the £ scale. 36DM is worth £12.

The results of a mathematics test for a group of students are shown in the table below:

Mark	0	1	2	3	4	5	6	7	8	9	10
Number of students	0	0	0	1	0	2	5	6	8	2	1

(i) How many students are there in the group?

(ii) What is the mean mark?

(iii) What is the median mark?

(iv) What is the modal mark?

Solution

(i) Number of students is

$$1+2+5+6+8+2+1 = 25$$

(ii) To get the mean we must find the total of all the marks the 25 students got and then divide by 25. Obviously we only consider those marks actually achieved by a student. The total of the marks, as shown in the table on the right, is 177, so

mean mark $= \frac{177}{25}$

$= 7.08$

Mark	No. of students	Total of marks
3	1	3
5	2	10
6	5	30
7	6	42
8	8	64
9	2	18
10	1	10
Total		177

Mark	No. of students	Running total
10	1	1
9	2	3
8	8	11
7	6	17
6	5	22
5	2	24
3	1	25

(iii) The median mark is the middle mark when they are arranged in order. As there are 25 students the middle one is the 13th (12 on either side).
As can be seen from the table on the left, the 13th student is in the group who got 7, so the median mark = 7.

(iv) The modal mark is the most common mark. So the modal mark = 8.

(Which of these represents the data best? It depends upon the reason for wanting a typical value. For example, if we had shoe sizes we would probably be more interested in the modal shoe size than the mean size.)

Do It Yourself

'Coordinates can be thought of as an address, information which tells you where you are on the graph'

1 Draw each of the following two graphs on the same graph paper. What are the coordinates of the point where they cross?
(i) $y = x + 2$ (ii) $y = 2 - x$

2 Look at the following table for $y = x^2$:

x	−3	−2	−1	0	1	2	3
$y = x^2$	9			0	1		

(i) Copy and complete the table.
(ii) Draw the graph of $y = x^2$ for x from −3 to 3.
(iii) Use the graph to find the square of 1.8 and also the square root of 7.

A patient's temperature is taken every three hours for a day. Plot these readings on a graph, with the *x*-axis for time, marked every 3 hours, and the *Y*-axis for temperature, with the scale going from 95°F to 105°F.

Time	0	3	6	9	12	15	18	21
Temperature	102	102	100.5	99.5	99	99.5	99	98

Connect up the points with straight lines to give an indication of how the temperature of the patient changes. Is it possible to predict the next temperature reading? Why?

a Josh did a traffic survey to count the number of vehicles passing by his home. He produced the following tally table:

Vehicle type	Tally
Cars	JHT JHT JHT JHT IIII
Lorries	JHT III
Vans	JHT JHT JHT III
Motorcycles	JHT JHT II
Cycles	JHT III

(i) How many of each type of vehicle are there?
(ii) How many vehicles are there altogether?

b Here is the start of the book *Treasure Island*, by Robert Louis Stevenson:
'Squire Trelawney, Dr. Livesey, and the rest of the gentlemen having asked me to write down the whole particulars . . .'

Draw up a tally chart for the first 50 letters, showing their frequency – ignore any letters not used (like *x*).

5 The milkman delivers the following numbers of pints of milk on one day to the houses in Jubilee Road:

No. of pints delivered	0	1	2	3	4	5
No. of houses	4	9	16	7	3	1

(i) Draw a frequency chart to illustrate these data.
(ii) How many houses are there in Jubilee Road?
(iii) How many houses received just one pint of milk on this day?
(iv) How many pints of milk were delivered to Jubilee Road?
(v) What is the average consumption of milk in pints per house?

6 A survey was carried out to find out what people used to heat their houses. The results are shown in the table on the right:

(i) How many houses were surveyed?
(ii) Draw a pie chart to illustrate the information.

Fuel	No. of houses
Coal	40
Electricity	80
Gas	145
Oil	95

7 Draw a graph to convert between gallons and litres, given that 1 gallon is 4.5 litres. Allow your gallon scale to go up to 10 gallons. Using your graph convert:

(i) 4 gallons to litres   (ii) 27 litres to gallons
(iii) $5\frac{1}{2}$ gallons to litres   (iv) 33 litres to gallons

8 Nine pupils had their height measured in centimetres. Here are the results:

169   162   176   166   162   178   185   169   162

Find:
(i) the mean height;   (ii) the median height;   (iii) the modal height.

Time, Speed and Travel Graphs

Things You Need to Know

1 **Time** can be given in either 12-hour form or 24-hour form. In the 24-hour form we always give four figures – two for the hours and two for the minutes. You should get used to adding/subtracting 12 to/from the hours when converting between the 12- and 24-hour systems. As a reminder, here is a table showing some typical times from midnight through the day to midnight again:

Midnight	3.00 a.m.	5.30 a.m.	7.45 a.m.	9.00 a.m.	10.00 a.m.	Midday	1.00 p.m.
00.00	03.00	05.30	07.45	09.00	10.00	12.00	13.00
2.45 p.m.	3.35 p.m.	6.00 p.m.	7.05 p.m.	8.00 p.m.	9.30 p.m.	11.00 p.m.	Midnight
14.45	15.35	18.00	19.05	20.00	21.30	23.00	00.00

2 **Speed** is simply how fast you are travelling. There are two sorts of measures – speed and average speed.

(i) Speed measures your speed at a particular moment. In other words, if you continued travelling at the same rate, you would cover that distance in 1 hour. A speedometer gives this speed.

(ii) Average speed $= \dfrac{\text{total distance travelled}}{\text{total time taken}}$

This gives a single speed for the whole journey – it allows for the fact that you might speed up and slow down.

'Note that you do not find the average speed by finding the mean of a group of speeds'

3 A **travel graph** (or **distance– time graph**) shows the way the distance from some place (usually where you started from) changes as the journey occurs. A typical graph showing the journey a boy made to the supermarket and back is given here with his commentary:

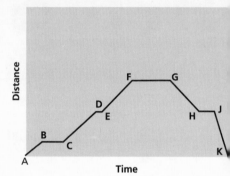

A – left home

A to B – walked towards supermarket

B to C – met someone and had a chat

C to D – continued on

D to E – had to wait to cross a road

E to F – crossed the road and walked through a large car park

F to G – arrived at the supermarket and did the shopping

G to H – left the supermarket and headed back through the car park

H to J – came to the road and waited to cross

J to K – crossed the road and continued homeward, but now more quickly (it steeper)

K – arrived home

ow to Do It

A cake takes 20 minutes to prepare, $2\frac{3}{4}$ hours to bake, 1 hour to cool and 45 minutes to decorate. If Zoë wants the cake to be finished by 3.00 p.m., what is the latest time that she must start the cake?

Solution
Method 1
One way is with a time line, working backwards from 3.00 p.m.

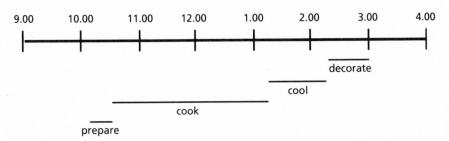

So it should be started by 10.10 a.m.

Method 2
Or, the time taken to get the cake done is

$$0.20 + 2.45 + 1.00 + 0.45 = 4 \text{ hours } 50 \text{ minutes}$$

So 4 hours 50 minutes before 3.00 p.m. (call it 5 hours and then sort out the 10 minutes at the end) gives 10.00. Now add the 10 minutes to give 10.10 a.m. at the latest.

Two drivers start a journey. In the first 10 minutes Bill covers 8 km, whereas Sally covers 13 km in the first 15 minutes. Who is the faster driver?

Solution
Bill: 8 km in 10 minutes $= \frac{8}{10}$ km in 1 minute
$$= \frac{8}{10} \times 60 \text{ km in 1 hour}$$

So Bill is travelling at 48 km/hour.

Sally: 13 km in 15 minutes $= \frac{13}{15}$ km in 1 minute
$$= \frac{13}{15} \times 60 \text{ km in 1 hour}$$

So Sally is travelling at 52 km/hour. Therefore Sally is the faster driver.

3 Alan started to cycle from home to college, a distance of 10 miles, at 8.15 a.m. After half an hour he had covered 6 miles when he had a puncture. It took him 45 minutes to get the puncture repaired. He then made good time and covered the remaining 4 miles in 15 minutes. Draw a distance–time graph of the journey. What time did Alan arrive at college? What was his average speed?

Solution

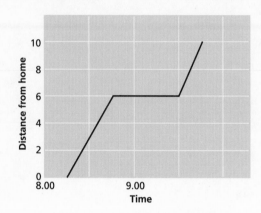

From the graph Alan arrived at the college at 9.45 a.m.

His average speed = total distance/total time taken

$$= \frac{10}{1\frac{1}{2}}$$

$$= 6\frac{2}{3} \text{ miles/hour} \quad (6.67 \text{ miles/hour to two decimal places})$$

Do It Yourself

1 a The time is five thirty in the afternoon. Write this time:
   (i) in a.m./p.m. time;
   (ii) in 24-hour time.

b A coach leaves Bristol at 09.45 to travel to Aberdeen. The journey takes $8\frac{1}{4}$ hours. What time does the coach arrive in Aberdeen?

c One day this summer, sunrise was at 06.32 and sunset was at 19.13. How long was the sun up?

2 Mark left home at 6.30 a.m. to travel to the airport 115 km away. He travelled the first 15 km at an average speed of 45 km/hour and the rest at an average speed of 40 km/hour.
(i) At what time did he arrive, assuming he did not stop?
(ii) What was his average speed for the whole journey?

3 The graph shows Terry's journey to school. She walked from her home to the bus stop, waited and then caught the bus to school.

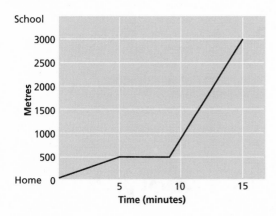

(i) How long did it take her to get to school?
(ii) How long did she wait at the bus stop?
(iii) How far from home was she after 12 minutes?
(iv) How far is it from the bus stop to school?
(v) What was her average speed in metres per minute?

11 | Angles and Triangles

Things You Need to Know

1 We measure angles in degrees (written as °). In a full turn (or circle) there are 360°. Some angles have special names: A **right** angle is 90°.

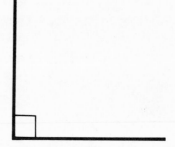

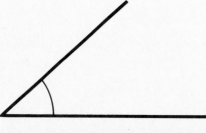

An **acute** angle is less than 90°.

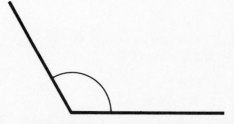

An **obtuse** angle is greater than 90° and less than 180°.

A straight line (or half-turn) is 180°.

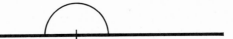

A **reflex** angle is greater than 180°.

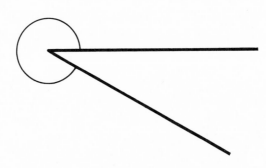

2 Angles are measured with a protractor – take care to use the correct scale and don't forget the intelligent estimate.

3 When two straight lines cross, four angles are formed, but there are only two different sizes of angle:

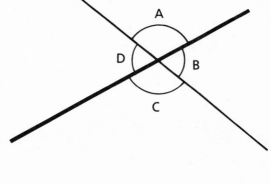

The angles A and C are equal in size and the angles B and D are equal in size. (Another way of saying it is that opposite angles are equal.)

4 Two straight lines that never cross no matter how far they are drawn are called **parallel** lines. (We mark them with arrows.) Here is a pair of parallel lines:

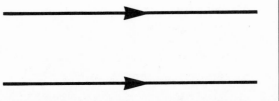

'Making intelligent estimates of the size of angles is quite important – it may help you to decide if an answer/ diagram is correct'

'All lines marked with the same number of arrows are parallel'

If a straight line crosses a pair of parallel lines, as shown on the right, the opposite angles are equal.

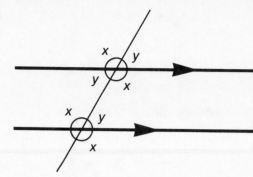

5 A line at right angles to another is **perpendicular**. (Note that the angle on either side is 90°, and remember that the angles on a straight line total 180°: $2 \times 90°$.)

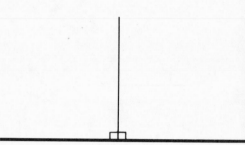

6 A triangle is a shape with three straight sides and three angles; the angles add up to give 180°.

The **perimeter** of a triangle is the distance all the way round it. To find the perimeter, add the lengths of the three sides together.

A triangle happens to be the shape with the smallest number of sides/angles and is very important (one reason is that if it is made up from strips it is rigid, unlike any other shape made up from strips). There are some types of triangle that are important:

Scalene triangle (all sides different lengths, all angles different)

Acute-angled triangle (all angles less than 90°)

Right-angled triangle (one angle 90°)

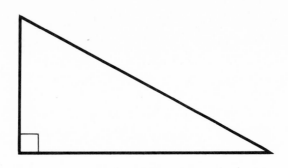

Obtuse-angled triangle (one angle larger than 90°)

Equilateral triangle (all sides the same length, all angles the same: 60°)

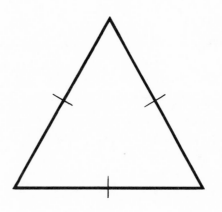

'When sides are the same length they are marked with a small line'

Isosceles triangle (two sides the same length, and the two angles opposite the equal sides equal)

In an isosceles triangle, a line drawn from the angle made by the two equal sides down to the middle of the third side is perpendicular to the third side and cuts the angle in half.

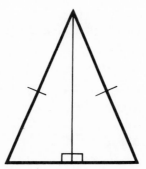

'*Use a sharp pencil, a pair of compasses, a protractor and a ruler to draw the triangle*'

7 In order to draw a triangle it is not necessary to know the lengths of all three sides and the sizes of all three angles – all you need are three measurements, at least one of which is a length. It is possible to draw a triangle given any of the following:
  (i) the lengths of the three sides; or
 (ii) the lengths of two sides and the angle between them; or
(iii) two angles and the length of one side.
    When asked to draw a triangle always draw a rough diagram. Try to get the angles about right and the sides roughly to scale.

How to Do It

1 Describe the types of angles marked in the diagrams below:

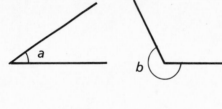

Solution

a acute	*d* obtuse
b reflex	*e* acute
c obtuse	

2 Estimate the sizes of the angles marked in the diagram for question 1 and then measure the angles with a protractor.

Solution

Angle	a	b	c	d	e
Estimate	40°	230°	150°	110°	35°
Measured	33°	244°	150°	120°	31°

(Your estimates will probably be slightly different from those shown here.)

Find the angles *x*, *y* and *z* in the following diagram:

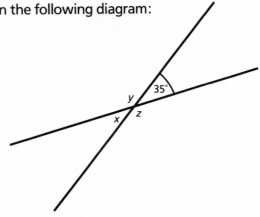

Solution

$$x = 35° \qquad \text{(opposite 35° angle)}$$
$$y + 35° = 180° \qquad \text{(angles on straight line)}$$
$$y = 145°$$
$$z = 145° \qquad \text{(opposite } y\text{)}$$

Find the angles marked *x*, *y* and *z* in the following diagram:

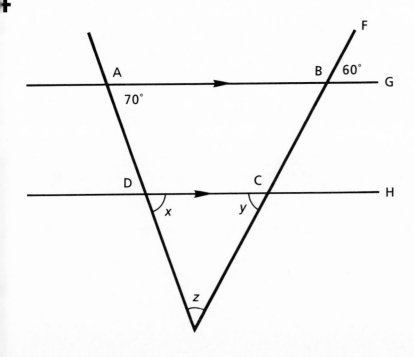

Solution

Since angle x is in a similar position to the angle of 70° (angle BAD)

$$x = 70°$$

The angle BCH is in a similar position to the angle of 60° (angle FBG), so angle BCH = 60°. Angle y is opposite angle BCH, so

$$y = 60°$$

The angles of any triangle total 180°, so

$$x + y + z = 180°$$
$$70° + 60° + z = 180°$$
$$z = 50°$$

5 In the following diagram, find which pairs of lines are perpendicular.

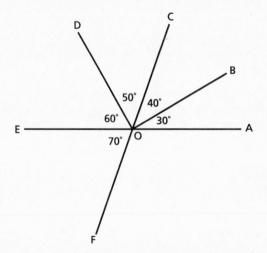

Solution

The method here is to look to see if any neighbouring angles total 90°.
$$40° + 50° = 90°$$

So lines OB and OD are perpendicular.

Angle AOF needs calculating to check if it is 90°

Angle AOF $= 360° - (70° + 60° + 50° + 40° + 30°)$
$= 110°$ (so *not* a right angle)

The only lines perpendicular in the diagram are OB and OD.

In the following diagram find all the unknown angles:

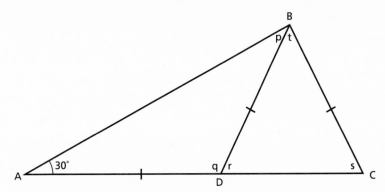

For each of the three triangles ABC, ABD and BCD, state what type of triangle it is.

Solution
First, draw your own copy of the triangle.

In triangle ABD:

$$\text{since } AD = BD \text{ then } p = 30°$$
$$30° + p + q = 180° \quad \text{(angles of triangle)}$$
$$q = 180° - 30° - 30°$$
$$q = 120°$$

$$q + r = 180° \quad \text{(angles on a straight line)}$$
$$r = 180° - 120°$$
$$r = 60°$$

In triangle BCD:

$$\text{since } BC = BD \text{ then } s = 60°$$
$$r + s + t = 180° \quad \text{(angles of triangle)}$$
$$t = 180° - 60° - 60°$$
$$t = 60°$$

Triangle ABD is an isosceles triangle.
Triangle BCD is an equilateral triangle.
Triangle ABC is a right-angled triangle $(p + t = 90°)$.

7 Draw a triangle ABC with

AB = 6 cm   BC = 8 cm   and   AC = 10 cm

Measure the angles of the triangle.

Solution

Firstly draw a sketch, as shown on the right. This is not an accurate sketch, but it does give an idea of how the sides of the triangle are set out, together with their lengths – which saves having to reread the question!

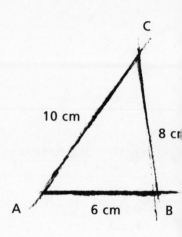

Now draw it accurately, as shown below right.

Angle A = 53°
Angle B = 90°
Angle C = 37°

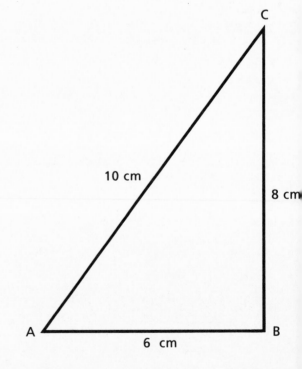

o It Yourself

Here is a diagram of a rectangle with its diagonals drawn in; these intersect at O.

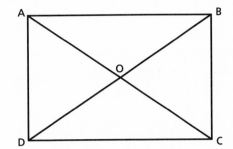

In the diagram find:

    (i) a right angle
    (ii) an acute angle
    (iii) an obtuse angle
    (iv) a reflex angle
    (v) a straight-line angle   (i.e. 180°)

On a piece of squared paper, draw a rectangle ABCD with sides AB = 4 units and BC = 7 units. Draw in the diagonals and label their intersection O. Measure the size of:

    (i) angle ABD
    (ii) angle BOC
    (iii) reflex angle COD
    (iv) angle DAO

Two lines cross. The larger angle formed is three times the smaller. Find the size of the smaller angle.

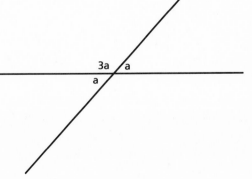

Find the angles a and b marked on the diagram.

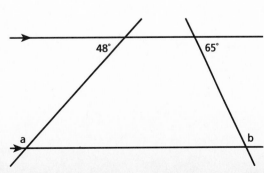

5 In the diagram find at least four right angles.

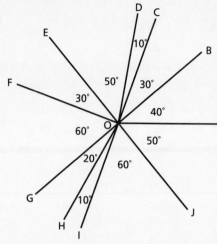

6 For each of the triangles ABC below and opposite, state what type of triangle it is, and answer the question by the diagram.

(i) What can you say about $x + y$?

(ii) What is the relationship of x and y?

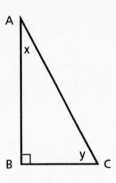

(iii) What does the line AD do to the line BC?

(iv) What is the size of angle x?

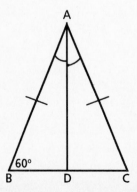

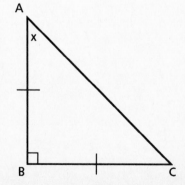

(v) What is the size of angle *x*?

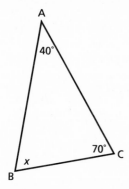

(vi) Which is the longest side?

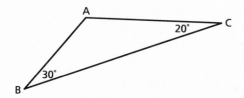

7 a Construct the triangle XYZ in which XY = 3.5 cm, YZ = 5 cm and XZ = 4 cm. Measure the angle XZY.

 b Construct the triangle ABC with AB = 4 cm, AC = 5 cm and angle CAB = 45°. Measure the length of BC.

 c Construct the triangle LMN in which LM = 8 cm, angle LMN = 40° and angle NLM = 70°. Measure the length of MN.

12 Quadrilaterals and Polygons

Things You Need to Know

1 A **quadrilateral** is a shape made up of four straight sides. There are special names for some of them:

Trapezium
(one pair of parallel sides)

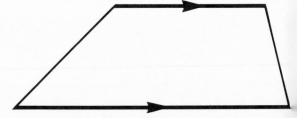

Parallelogram
(opposite sides parallel,
opposite sides equal in length,
diagonally opposite angles
equal)

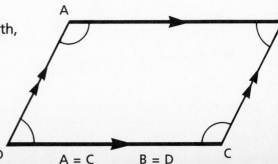

Rectangle
(A special parallelogram with
angles of 90°, opposite sides
equal, diagonals equal)

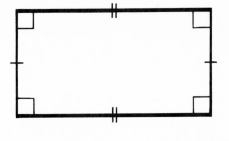

Square
(a rectangle with all sides the
same length)

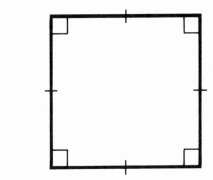

Rhombus
(a parallelogram with all sides
equal in length

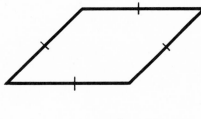

Kite
(two pairs of adjacent sides
equal)

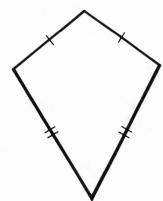

It is possible to draw other quadrilaterals, but they are not special in any
way. However, whatever the quadrilateral, the angles will always add
up to 360°.

2 A **polygon** is a shape made up of straight sides – it could have three side (a triangle) or it could have four sides (a quadrilateral) or it could have more as shown in the following diagrams. (There are names for others, bu these are the main ones.)

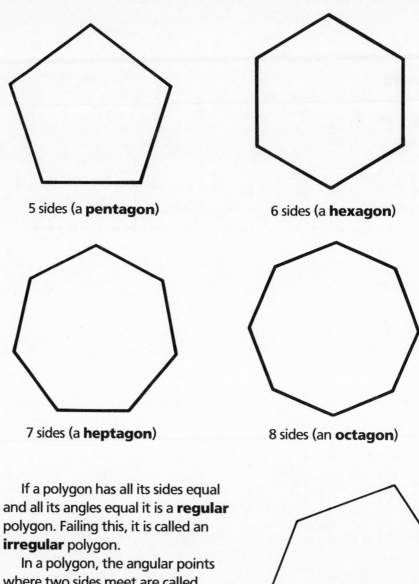

5 sides (a **pentagon**)   6 sides (a **hexagon**)

7 sides (a **heptagon**)   8 sides (an **octagon**)

If a polygon has all its sides equal and all its angles equal it is a **regular** polygon. Failing this, it is called an **irregular** polygon.

In a polygon, the angular points where two sides meet are called **vertices**; one is called a **vertex**. A line joining two vertices is known as a **diagonal**. For example, a pentagon has five diagonals.

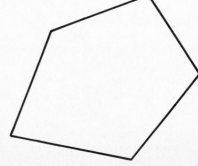

How to Do It

In the following diagram, ABCD is a trapezium and CDEF is a square. What is the size of the angle marked *x*?

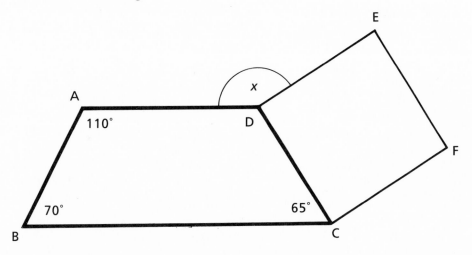

Solution

Since the angles of a quadrilateral total 360°

$$110° + 70° + 65° + D = 360°$$
$$D = 115°$$

The angle at D inside the square is 90° and all the angles around a point total 360°, so

$$\text{angle D} + \text{angle CDE} + x = 360°$$
$$115° + 90° + x = 360°$$
$$x = 155°$$

2 In the following diagram and using the labels provided:
   (i) Pick out
      (a) a pentagon   (c) a heptagon
      (b) a hexagon   (d) an octagon
   (ii) State the name of the shape CDEF.
   (iii) Are all the shapes listed in (i) and (ii) regular or irregular?

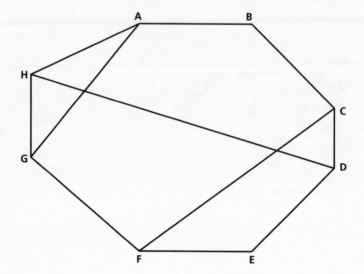

Solution

   (i) (a) ABCFG (or ABCDH or DEFGH) (5 straight sides)
      (b) ABCFGH (6 straight sides)
      (c) ABCDEFG (7 straight sides)
      (d) ABCDEFGH (8 straight sides)
   (ii) CDEF is a quadrilateral (4 straight sides)
   (iii) irregular (all sides and angles not equal)

Do It Yourself

1 **a** Find the angles *a* and *b* in the diagram:

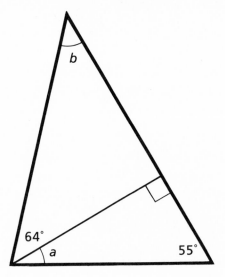

b Find the angles *c*, *d* and *e* in the diagram:

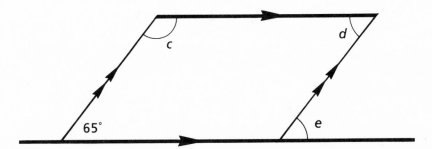

2 Draw sketches of a triangle, a quadrilateral, a pentagon, a hexagon and an octagon with all the diagonals drawn in. (The diagonals of a pentagon have been drawn for you.) For each, state how many diagonals it has. How many diagonals would you predict for a nine-sided figure?

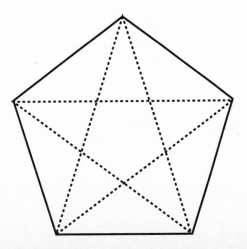

13 | Circles

Things You Need to Know

1 Circles have special words indicating important parts or points:

Centre
(the point where you put the point of the compasses; it is the same distance from any point on the circle)

Circumference
(the distance all the way round the circle)

Diameter
(any straight line through the centre between two points on the circle)

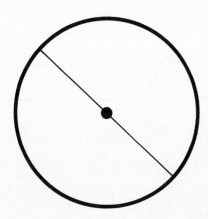

Semicircle
(either of the two halves the diameter divides the circle into)

Radius
(a line from the centre to any
point on the circle)

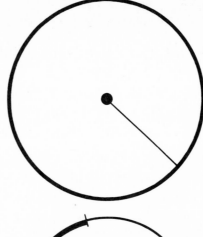

Arc
(a part of the circumference)

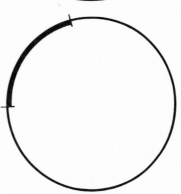

2 The circumference and the diameter/radius are connected by the number
given the symbol π (pronounced 'pi'):

Circumference $= \pi \times d$

or

circumference $= 2 \times \pi \times r$

where d means diameter and r means radius.
   π is the number 3.141 592 653 589 793 238 4626 . . . and so on. It
continues for ever without any pattern. We normally use the value 3.14 or
even $\frac{22}{7}$ (sometimes given as $3\frac{1}{7}$) – but you will be told what value to use.

*'Many
calculators
have a pi
button to help
with the
calculations
connected
with the circle'*

How to Do It

1 On the diagram below, parts of the circle are labelled. Give the name of each part:

Solution

    O is the centre
    r is the radius
    d is the diameter
    x is an arc

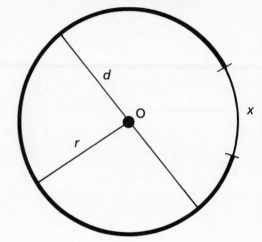

2 On Sam's watch the minute hand is 1.2 cm long and the hour hand is 0.8 cm long. How far does the tip of each hand move in 1 hour? (Use $\pi = 3.14$.)

Solution

Minute hand: this does one complete turn in 1 hour so distance travelled is

    $2 \times \pi \times 1.2\,\text{cm} = 7.536\,\text{cm}$
                       $= 7.54\,\text{cm}$ (correct to two decimal places)

Hour hand: if it did one complete turn it would travel

    $2 \times \pi \times 0.8\,\text{cm} = 5.024\,\text{cm}$

However, it only travels $\frac{1}{12}$th of this in 1 hour, so distance travelled is

    $\frac{5.024}{12}\,\text{cm} = 0.419\,\text{cm}$
                    $= 0.42\,\text{cm}$ (correct to two decimal places)

Do It Yourself

Unless told differently, for the following questions use $\pi = 3.14$.

1 Here is a circle. Give the label(s) for each of the following and find the measurement asked for (in millimetres).

(i) the centre and the length of the radius

(ii) a chord and its length

(iii) a diameter and its length

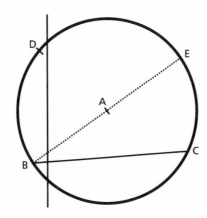

2 a If the distance round a circular bowl is 28 cm, find its radius correct to one decimal place.

b A circular patio has a radius of 2.5 m and is surrounded by a path of width 0.5 m. What is the difference in distance round the circle between the edge of the patio and the outer edge of the path?

c The diameter of a bicycle wheel is 50 cm.
(i) What is its radius?
(ii) How far will the bicycle move for one complete turn of the wheel?

d Here is a plan of the school athletics track. The inner radius of the track is 35 m and the track is 4 m wide.

(i) How far is it once round the inner track?
(ii) How far is it around the outer track?
(iii) Michael runs five times round the inside, while Joseph runs five times round the outside. Who runs further and by how much?

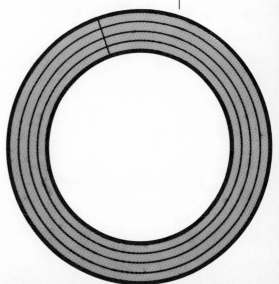

97

14

Transformation and Symmetry

Things You Need to Know

1 **Lines of symmetry** are balance lines, so that on each side of the line the shape is equally balanced. For example, the line x–y is a line of symmetry for the first shape, but not for the second shape:

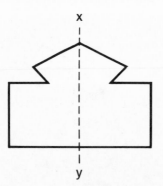

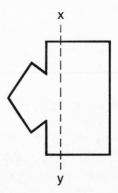

Some shapes may have more than one line of symmetry. If a shape has at least one line of symmetry, it is said to have **line symmetry**.

A shape can be reflected in a line (like in a mirror). For example, if we reflect the shape ABC in the **mirror line** x–y we get:

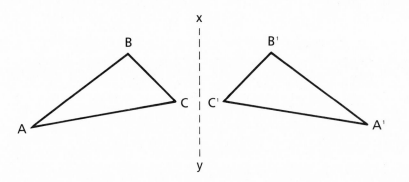

'*Notice how the direction of the letters ABC and A′ B′ C′ is different – the reflection is reversed, just like your face in a mirror*'

A shape can be rotated (or turned) about a point (the **centre of rotation**) in a given direction and by a given angle. The size of the object does not change with a rotation.

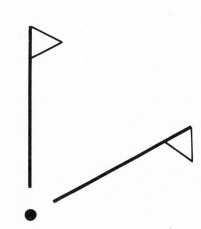

If we move the shape just by sliding it (not turning it over or around in any way) this is called a **translation**:

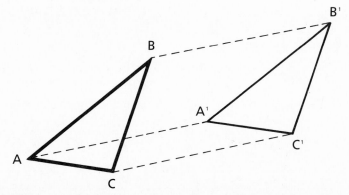

The lengths of the lines stay the same and so does the direction of the letters.

5 **Rotational symmetry** relies upon being able to turn the shape about some point so that it fits back upon itself, before the shape is completely turned round. The number of times it fits on itself is called the order of rotation.

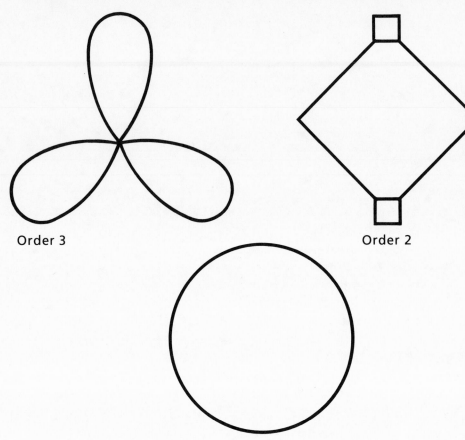

Order 3

Order 2

A very large number!! (called infinity)

6 **Similar** shapes are shapes that have the same shape but are different in size.

The **scale factor** is the ratio of a side to its corresponding side:

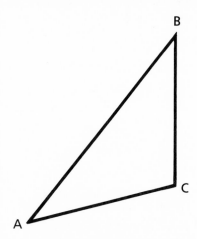
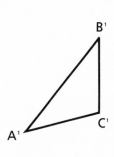

In going from ABC to A'B'C' the scale factor is $\frac{1}{2}$, and going from A'B'C' to ABC the scale factor is 2.

In order to find the scale factor, use:

$$\text{Scale factor} = \frac{\text{length of line on enlargement}}{\text{length of line on original}}$$

How to Do It

1 Complete the following diagram using the line of symmetry x–y:

Solution
This becomes the diagram
shown on the right.

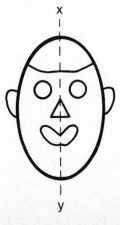

'A shape is symmetrical about a line when one half of it is a reflection of the other half'

101

2 Show what happens when the shape ABCD is first reflected in the line m—n to produce A'B'C'D', and then A'B'C'D' is reflected in the line x—y to give A''B''C''D''.

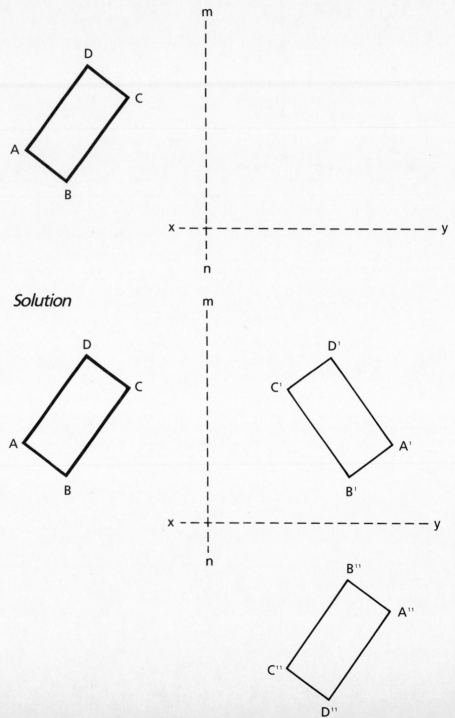

Solution

3 Sketch the result of rotating this shape 90° clockwise about P.

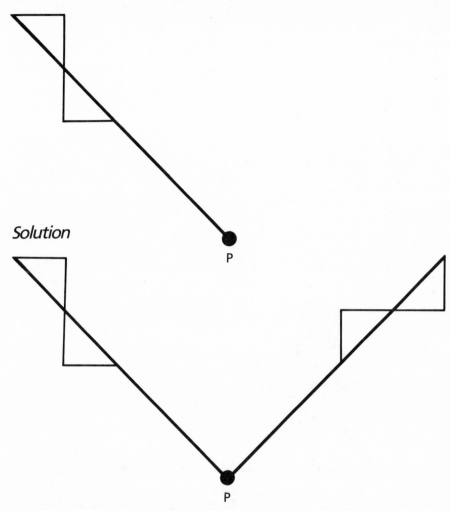

Solution

P

P

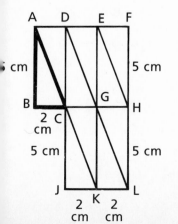

4 In the diagram on the left, where does the triangle ABC go if it is translated 4 cm to the right and 5 cm downwards?

Solution
It goes to GKL.

5 For each of the following letters state whether it has rotational symmetry. If it has, then state the order of rotation.

C H I N S

Solution

C has no rotational symmetry
H has rotational symmetry of order 2
I has rotational symmetry of order 2
N has rotational symmetry of order 2
S has rotational symmetry of order 2

6 The shadow of a tree is 4 m long and the shadow of a 75 cm stick is 25 cm long. How high is the tree?

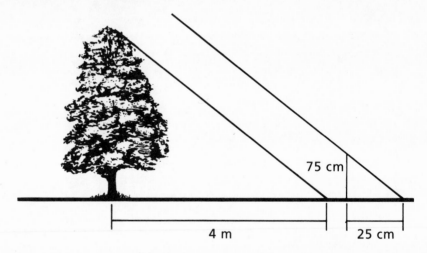

75 cm

4 m   25 cm

Solution
First, draw a sketch of the situation (remember it doesn't have to be accurate). The scale of enlargement is

$$\frac{4\,m}{25\,cm} = \frac{4}{0.25}$$
$$= 16$$

In other words, everything in the tree part is 16 times larger than in the stick part.
The height of the tree is

$$16 \times 75\,cm = 12\,m$$

Do It Yourself

Copy each of the following shapes and mark in their lines of symmetry.

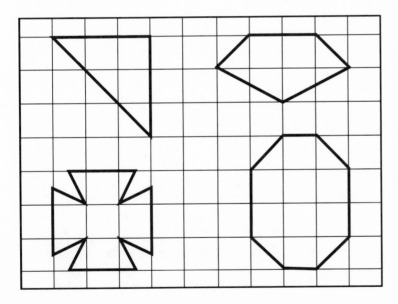

'Imagine folding the shape along the line – would the two halves 'fit together'? If 'yes', then it is a line of symmetry; if 'no', it is not a line of symmetry'

2 **a** Sketch the image of the figure when reflected in the dotted line.

(i)

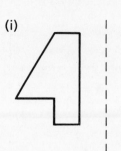

(ii)

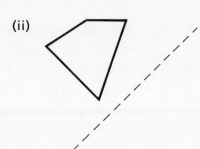

(iii)

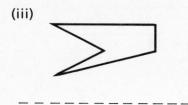

(iv)

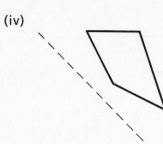

b Sketch the mirror line for the following diagrams:

(i)

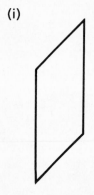 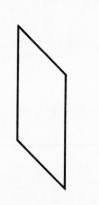

(ii)

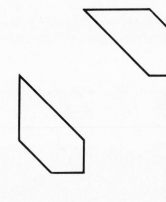

(iii)

 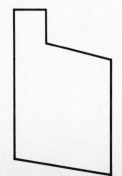

Copy the following shape on to squared paper and rotate it anticlockwise 135° about the point P. Measure the distance from A to A'.

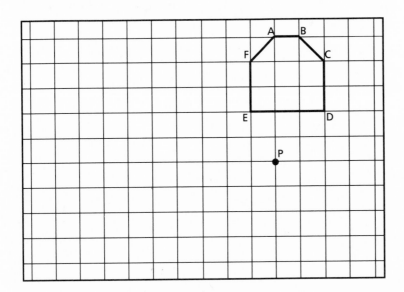

A rectangle ABCD has vertices (corners) A(1, 2), B(6, 2), C(6, 5) and D(1, 5). It is translated by 2 units to the right and 3 units up. Draw this on squared paper and state the coordinates of the vertices A', B', C' and D'. What is the length of the displacement from A to A'?

Plot each of the following sets of points on squared paper. Join them up in alphabetical order, and join the last to the first. State the order of rotational symmetry of the shape produced – if it does not have rotational symmetry then write 'none'.

    (i) A(4, 5), B(6, 5), C(6, 10) and D(4, 10)

   (ii) A(4, 10), B(8, 10), C(10, 15) and D(6, 15)

  (iii) A(0, 10), B(5, 5), C(10, 5), D(15, 10), E(15, 15), F(10, 20), G(5, 20) and
        H(0, 15)

  (iv) A(0, 5), B(5, 0), C(0, −5) and D(−5, 0)

6 **a** In the diagram, A'B'C' is an enlargement of ABC. What is the scale factor? On squared paper copy the drawing and then connect A to A' with a straight line and extend it beyond A. Do the same for B to B' and C to C'. What do you notice about the three straight lines?

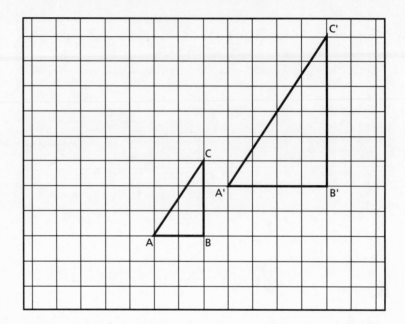

b Draw the rectangle ABCD on squared paper, with A(2, 3), B(6, 3), C(6, 7) and D(2, 7). With A' at the point (0, 0) draw the rectangle A'B'C'D', which is similar to ABCD and has a scale factor of 3 compared to ABCD. State the coordinates of the three vertices B', C' and D'.

Areas, Volumes and Solid Figures

15

Things You Need to Know

Shapes in the real world are usually three-dimensional. They are often made up of a series of simpler shapes like:

Cube
(all sides the same length, all angles 90°)

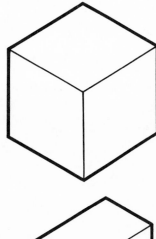

Cuboid
(opposite sides equal in length, all angles 90°)

Cylinder
(straight sides, and a same-size
circular cross-section)

Cone
(a circle at the bottom, tapering
to a point at the top)

Pyramid
(square-based, with four
triangular sides; or
triangular-based, made up of
just four triangles)

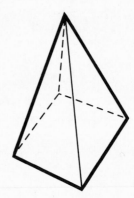

The flat surfaces of a solid are its **faces**, the 'lines' between one face and
another are called **edges** and the 'corners' where three or more edges
come to a point are called **vertices** (each one is called a **vertex**).

It is possible to arrange shapes on a sheet of paper that can be folded up to form a solid. The pattern of shapes on the paper is called the **net** of the solid. Here are a few examples of possible nets for a cube:

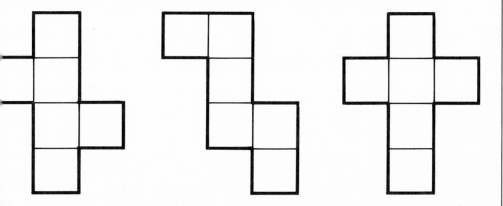

'It is interesting to see how many different ways six squares can be arranged together and find out how many of them are a net for a cube'

Area measures the space taken up by a surface. It is possible to get a rough idea of the area by covering it with squares and counting the squares. The units used depend upon the situation and might be

    square centimetres (cm²)
    square metres (m²)
    the hectare, which is 10 000 m²

Area of a rectangle = length × breadth

'The hectare is used for measuring land area in the metric system'

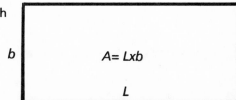

$A = Lxb$

Area of a triangle $= \frac{1}{2} \times$ base $\times$ height

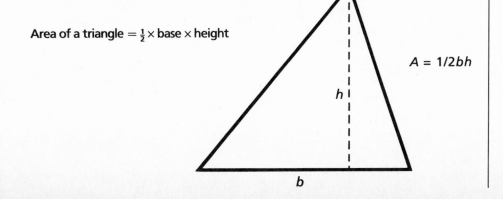

$A = 1/2bh$

4 **Volume** measures the capacity of a solid (how much it can hold). We use cubes to measure it. The units used are:

> cubic centimetre (cm³)
> cubic metre (m³)
> for liquids the litre (l), which is 1000 cm³

The only solid whose volume is easy to find is the cuboid:

> Volume of cuboid = length × breadth × height

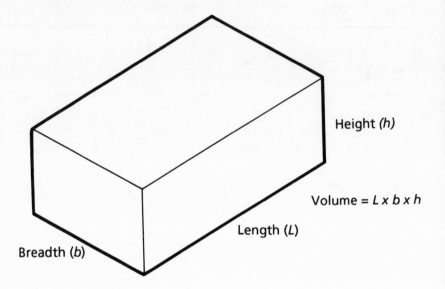

Height *(h)*

Volume = *L* x *b* x *h*

Length *(L)*

Breadth *(b)*

How to Do It

1 How many cubes have been put together to make this shape?

How many vertices, faces and edges does the shape have?

Solution

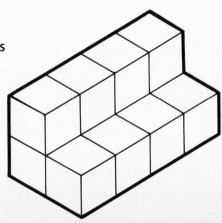

Number of cubes	= 12
Number of vertices	= 12
Number of faces	= 8
Number of edges	= 18

Which of the following nets could be folded up to form a complete cube?

(i)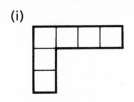

(ii)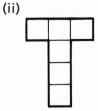

(iii)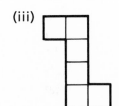

(iv)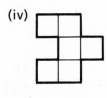

'If you cannot 'see' the cube, then get some squared paper, cut the nets out and try folding them into cubes'

Solution

(i) No   (ii) Yes   (iii) Yes   (iv) No

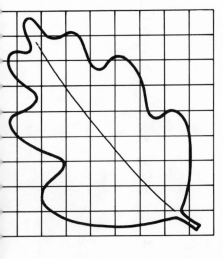

3 **a** Here is a drawing of a leaf on 1 cm squares. Approximately, what is the area of the leaf?

Solution

Marking complete squares and those that are at least half-covered by the leaf gives

There are 39 dots, so area = 39 cm².

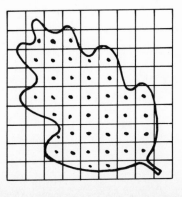

b A room is 4.5 m long and 5 m wide. If carpet costs £8.00 per square metre what is the cost of carpeting the room from wall to wall?

Solution

Area = 4.5 m × 5 m = 22.5 m²
Cost of carpet = £8.00 × 22.5 = £180.00

4 A box holding very small bars of chocolate is 3 cm by 2 cm by 6 cm; the small bars are 0.5 cm by 0.75 cm by 1 cm. How many small bars can I pack into the box?

Solution

6 bars will fit along the 6 cm length $\dfrac{6\,\text{cm}}{1\,\text{cm}}$

4 bars will fit along the 3 cm width $\dfrac{3\,\text{cm}}{0.75\,\text{cm}}$

4 bars will fit along the 2 cm height $\dfrac{2\,\text{cm}}{0.5\,\text{cm}}$

So the total number of bars = 6 × 4 × 4 = 96

Do It Yourself

1 Here is a cube made up of smaller cubes. There are 4 smaller cubes along each edge.
   (i) How many smaller cubes make up the larger cube?
   (ii) How many smaller cubes are completely hidden inside the larger cube?

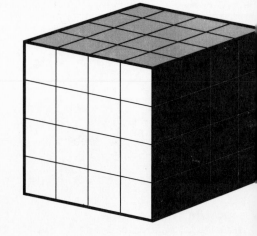

Name the shapes that can be made from the following nets:

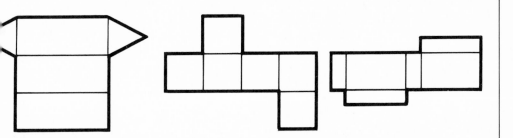

'It helps if you can 'see' in your imagination how the nets fold up to give the solid'

The diagram shows a square with a diagonal band, which is shaded.

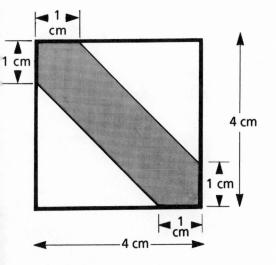

Find:

   (i) the perimeter of the square;

  (ii) the area of the square;

 (iii) the area unshaded;

 (iv) the area of the shaded band.

Brian's room is 4 m long, 3.5 m wide and 3 m high.

  (i) What is the total area of the walls? (Ignore windows and doors.)

 (ii) What is the area of the ceiling?

(iii) What is the volume of the room?

16 Algebra

Things You Need to Know

1 Often when we don't actually know a particular value (e.g. the length of
line) we use a letter to stand for the value – this is the basis of algebra.
Always use a letter which helps remind you of what it represents (e.g. *L* fc
length, *h* for height).

Some of the basic facts of algebra are given below:

(i) *a* means just the value of 1*a* or '1 times *a*'

(ii) 3*x* means '3 times *x*'

(iii) $\dfrac{n}{2}$ means '*n* divided by 2' or '$\frac{1}{2}$ of *n*'

(iv) *bc* means '*b* times *c*'

(v) 2*bh* means '2 times *b* times *h*'

(vi) t^2 means '*t* times *t*'

(vii) $5x^2$ means '5 times x^2' or '5 times *x* times *x*'

(viii) $(3p)^2$ means '3*p* times 3*p*' or '3 times 3 times *p* times *p*'. This is not
the same as $3p^2$, which means '3 times p^2', or '3 times *p* times *p*'.

(ix) *a*(*b* + *c*) means *b* + *c* added together and *then* multiplied by *a*.
$(a + b)^2$ means *a* and *b* added together and then squared.

We often use letters to make a formula that represents a rule for doing
a calculation, like: Area of a triangle = $\frac{1}{2}bh$

When rearranging an equation or formula you must ensure that what is done to one side of the equals sign is similarly done to the other side. For example, if you add 7 to one side you must add 7 to the other side too (otherwise the equal sign is no longer true!).

The way to solve an equation is to rearrange it so that the letter terms are on one side only and the number terms are on the other. For example:

$$7x+9 = 30 \quad \text{(now subtract 9 from each side)}$$
$$7x+9-9 = 30-9$$
$$7x = 21 \quad \text{(now divide each side by 7)}$$
$$x = 3$$

Equations often arise when solving problems and are a way of summarising the problem. Once an equation has been solved, this result can then be used to find the answers to the original problem. For example, if 15 articles are bought, some of which cost 5p each and the rest cost 8p each, and if the total amount spent is 90p, how many of each article are bought?

To solve this, let x be the number of 5p articles. Then $(15-x)$ is the number of 8p articles. So

$$5x+8(15-x) = 90$$
$$5x+120-8x = 90$$
$$120-3x = 90$$
$$30 = 3x$$
$$x = 10$$

Therefore, 10 of them cost 5p and 5 of them cost 8p.

Note: It is a good idea to check that it works:

$$10 \times 5\text{p}+5 \times 8\text{p} = 90\text{p}$$

‘You must always do the same thing to both sides of an equation so that it stays ‘balanced’’

How to Do It

1 **a** If Andy has £10 more than Brian, how much do they have altogether if Brian has £b?

Solution
Since Brian has £b, Andy must have £$(b+10)$ as he has £10 more than Brian. So altogether they have

$$£b+£(b+10) = £(2b+10)$$

b If $a = 3$ and $b = -4$, what is the value of a^2-3b+8?

Solution
Just fit the values in the formula:

$$a = 3 \qquad b = -4$$

$$\begin{aligned} a^2-3b+8 &= 3^2-3(-4)+8 \\ &= 9-(-12)+8 \quad \text{(careful with the signs!)} \\ &= 9+12+8 \\ &= 29 \end{aligned}$$

2 Solve the equation $7x-11 = 13-x$.

Solution

$$\begin{aligned} 7x-11 &= 13-x \quad \text{(now add } x \text{ to each side)} \\ 7x+x-11 &= 13-x+x \\ 8x-11 &= 13 \quad \text{(now add 11 to each side)} \\ 8x-11+11 &= 13+11 \\ 8x &= 24 \quad \text{(now divide by 8)} \\ x &= 3 \end{aligned}$$

Check it with the original equation (LHS = left-hand side; RHS = right-hand side)

$$\text{LHS: } 7x-11 = 21-11 = 10$$

$$\text{RHS: } 13-x = 13-3 = 10$$

Since LHS = RHS it is correct.

£380 is divided between Annie and Brian. If Annie receives £144 more than Brian, how much does each receive?

Solution
Let b represent the amount that Brian receives, so Annie get £$(b+144)$

$$\text{thus} \quad b+(b+144) = 380$$
$$b+b+144 = 380$$
$$2b+144 = 380$$
$$2b = 236$$
$$= 118$$

So Brian gets £118 and Annie gets £118 + 144 = £262,

Do It Yourself

a Given that $a = 4$, $b = 2$, $c = -5$ and $d = 0$, find:
  (i) a^2 (ii) $2b^2$ (iii) $(4c)^2$ (iv) $(a-b)^2$
  (v) a^2-b^2 (vi) $ab-cd$ (vii) a^2b (viii) $abcd$

b Simplify the following:
  (i) $2a+6a+a$ (ii) $7a-2a$
  (iii) $6x+7y-2x-y$ (iv) $a^2+2a-3a^2-4a$
  (v) $3a$ times $7a$ (vi) $3xy$ times $4xy$

Solve these equations:
  (i) $5x = 10$ (ii) $x+5 = 12$
  (iii) $17-3x = 2$ (iv) $4(m+3) = 20$

a Jason thinks of a number, subtracts 6 from it and multiplies the result by 3; the answer is 27.
  (i) Write down the equation representing the situation.
  (ii) What was the number he thought of?

b The sides of a triangle are such that one side is 4 cm shorter than the base side and the other side is 2 cm longer than the base side. If x cm represents the length of the base side and the perimeter is 46 cm:
  (i) write down an equation representing the situation
  (ii) find the length of each side of the triangle.

Answers

Section 1

1 **a** (i) 9300   (ii) 9330   (iii) 9326.69
    (i) 100   (ii) 85.5   (iii) 85.51
    (i) 200   (ii) 227   (iii) 227.25

    b (i) 2.65   (ii) 6.63   (iii) 0.56
    (iv) 9.87

    c £3.57

    d (i) 27 499   (ii) 26 500

2 **a** 2, 3, 4, 6, 12

    b (i) 1, 2, 4, 5, 8, 10, 20   (ii) 2, 4, 8

3 **a** 11 and 5

    b 7 and 5

4 **a** 3   6   9   12   15   18   21   24   27   30   33   36
      3   6   9   3   6   9   3   6   9   3   6   9
      It goes 3, 6, 9 or it always adds up to a multiple of 3.

    b (i) 7, 14, 21, 28, 35, 42, 49, 56, 63, 70, 77, 84, 91, 98
      (ii) 14, 28, 42, 56, 70, 84, 98
      They are multiples of 14.

5 (i) −4   (ii) −14   (iii) 9
    (iv) −2   (v) 28   (vi) −7

6 **a** (iii) 6 and 7   (iv) 5 and 6   (v) 4 and 5   (vi) 5 and 6
    (vii) 25 and 36 (could make a better guess of 30 and 36)
    (viii) 64 and 81 (could guess something like 75 and 81)

    b (i) 5   (ii) 3   (iii) 12   (iv) 13

Section 2

1 **a** (i) 15, 18   (ii) 64, 128   (iii) 37, 47
    (iv) 4, 2

    b (i) (a) 5, 13, 41, 61   (b) 25
      (ii) 8, 12, 16, 20   (goes up by 4 each time)
      (iii) 85, 113   (add 24, then add 28)

2 1, 3, 6, 10, 15, 21
    (i) 3   (ii) 10, 15   (iii) 3, 6, 15, 21

3 (i) S_2 (ii) S_5 (iii) S_6
    (iv) S_7

4 64   125   216   343   512   729   1000   1331
      61   91   127   169   217   271   331
      24   30   36   42   48   54   60
    6   6   6   6   6   6   6
    Yes, $11^3 = 1331$.

5 These are sample answers; your choice of numbers from
    the Fibonacci series might be different, but the principle
    is still correct.
    3   5   8 $3 \times 8 = 24$ $5^2 = 25$ (differ by 1)
    13   21   34 $13 \times 34 = 442$ $21^2 = 441$ (differ by 1)
    5   8   13 $5 \times 13 = 65$ $8^2 = 64$ (differ by 1)
    1   2   3 $1 \times 3 = 3$ $2^2 = 4$ (differ by 1)
    8   13   21 $8 \times 21 = 168$ $13^2 = 169$ (differ by 1)

6 (i) 36, 49 (square numbers)
    (ii) 8, 4 (each is half the previous one)
    (iii) 104, 416 (each is double the previous one)

ection 3

He lifts $\frac{3}{10}$, He doesn't lift $\frac{7}{10}$.

(i) Yes   (ii) No   (iii) No

(i) $\frac{1}{2}$ (ii) $\frac{1}{3}$ (iii) $\frac{1}{3}$
(iv) in lowest form   (v) $\frac{1}{5}$ (vi) $\frac{2}{3}$

$6\frac{3}{4}$

(i) $\frac{23}{5}$ (ii) $\frac{11}{7}$ (iii) $\frac{16}{3}$
(iv) $\frac{27}{4}$

a (i) $\frac{11}{15}$ (ii) $1\frac{3}{8}$ (iii) $\frac{43}{72}$ (iv) $4\frac{1}{8}$

b (i) $\frac{5}{12}$ (ii) $\frac{1}{24}$ (iii) $\frac{3}{20}$ (iv) $1\frac{4}{5}$

(i) $\frac{3}{28}$ (ii) $\frac{3}{5}$ (iii) $\frac{16}{27}$
(iv) $4\frac{7}{12}$

(i) $2\frac{1}{2}$ (ii) $2\frac{6}{7}$ (iii) $1\frac{5}{7}$
(iv) $\frac{21}{32}$

(Note: if $\frac{4}{5}$ of the distance is 16 miles then $\frac{1}{5}$ is 4 miles)
(i) 20 miles   (ii) 15 miles

b (i) £1.25   (ii) £0.62 or 62p   (iii) 2.40 m

c £31.45

d (i) £233.83   (ii) £108.69   (iii) £37.60

5 65% Grade B

6 (i) $\frac{1}{4}$ (ii) $\frac{3}{10}$ (iii) $\frac{9}{20}$
(iv) $\frac{1}{3}$ (v) $1\frac{1}{4}$

7 (i) 0.25   (ii) 0.43   (iii) 0.5
(iv) 0.8   (v) 1.2   (vi) 2.75

8 a 80%

b 10%

9 (i) 50%   (ii) 75%   (iii) 16%
(iv) 35%   (v) 174%

10 2.29

11 a (i) £12 : £36   (ii) 16 m : 12 m
(iii) 30 kg : 25 kg : 10 kg

b 6 m

ection 4

(i) 0.63   (ii) 0.7   (iii) 0.745
(iv) 0.03   (v) 0.012

(i) $\frac{3}{4}$ (ii) $\frac{31}{100}$ (iii) $\frac{1}{20}$
(iv) $\frac{33}{100}$ (v) $\frac{1}{8}$

(i) No. 3   (ii) No. 1   (iii) No. 5

a (80% of 50 litres = 40 litres)
600 km

Section 5

1 a Works $7\frac{1}{2}$ hours/day for a 5-day week –
earnings = £140.63 to nearest penny

b (i) $5\frac{1}{2}$ hours   (ii) £9.63 to nearest penny
(iii) 3 hours   (iv) £10.50   (v) £20.13

2 £3150

3 £133.36 to nearest penny

4 (Total paid back is £650) Interest = £50

5 £60

6 £67.53

7 Scheme A total is £530, scheme B total is £550 − scheme A charges less by £20.

2a (i) 46 mm   (ii) 79 mm   (iii) 9100 mm
(iv) 312 mm

b (i) 500 cm   (ii) 920 cm   (iii) 74 cm
(iv) 643.1 mm

c (i) 8 km   (ii) 0.4 km   (iii) 0.021 km

3a (i) 0.5 litres   (ii) 6 litres

b (i) 5200 ml   (ii) 750 ml

4 (i) 140 lb   (ii) 25 miles   (iii) 14 pints
(iv) 13 kg   (v) 56 km   (vi) 12 litres

Section 6

1 (i) 100 cm or 1 m   (ii) 5 m by 4 m
(iii) 3.5 cm by 2.5 cm

2a (i) 25 000 cm or 250 m or 0.25 km   (ii) 3 km
(iii) 16 cm

b 7.2 km

3 (i) 204 m   (ii) 257°

4 1 cm to $\frac{1}{4}$ km or 4 cm to 1 km or 1 : 25 000

Section 7

1a (i) 7.431 kg   (ii) 0.3761 kg   (iii) 2500 kg

b 34.5 kg

c 0.07 g   700 mg   70 g   0.7 kg

Section 8

1 (a) done in question;
(b) will definitely happen;
(c) will happen approximately $\frac{1}{10}$ th of the time in the long run;
(d) will happen about half the time in the long run.

2 $\frac{15}{50}$ or $\frac{3}{10}$ or 0.3

3a (i) $\frac{2}{11}$ (ii) $\frac{4}{11}$

b

	1	3	5	7
2	3	5	7	9
4	5	7	9	11
6	7	9	11	13
8	9	11	13	15

(i) $\frac{4}{16}$ or $\frac{1}{4}$ (ii) $\frac{6}{16}$ or $\frac{3}{8}$ (iii) 1

(iv) $\frac{6}{16}$ or $\frac{3}{8}$

(i) $\frac{26}{52}$ or $\frac{1}{2}$ or 0.5   (ii) $\frac{18}{30}$ or $\frac{3}{5}$ or 0.6

(iii) 0   (iv) $\frac{3}{9}$ or $\frac{1}{3}$ or 0.333 333 . . .

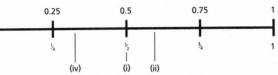

2 (i)

x	−3	−2	−1	0	1	2	3
$y = x^2$	9	4	1	0	1	4	9

(ii)

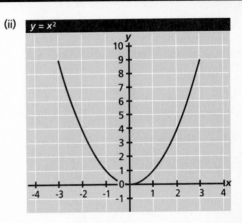

(iii) $1.8^2 = 3.2$ and the square root of 7 $= \pm 2.6$.

Note: For this degree of accuracy you would need to use a larger, more precise grid than the one shown here.

Section 9

(i)

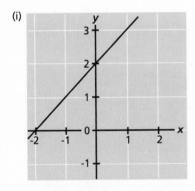

(ii)

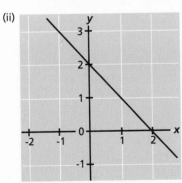

The coordinates of the points where they cross are (0, 2).

3

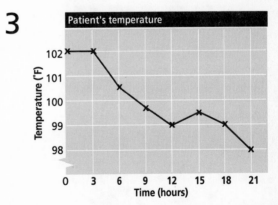

It is not possible to predict the next temperature reading as the patient's temperature does not necessarily follow a rule.

4 a (i) 24 cars, 8 lorries, 18 vans, 12 motorcycles, 8 cycles.
Total = 70 vehicles

b The totals for the letters are:

a. 3	d. 2	e. 11	f. 1	g. 1
h. 3	i. 2	l. 3	m. 1	n. 4
o. 1	q. 1	r. 4	s. 3	t. 5
u. 1	v. 1	w. 1	y. 2	

5 (i)

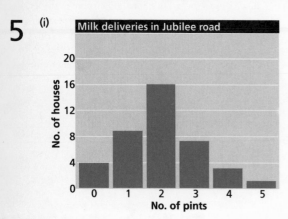

(ii) 40 houses   (iii) 9 houses   (iv) 79 pints
(v) $1\frac{39}{40}$ or 1.975

6 (i) 360 houses

(ii)

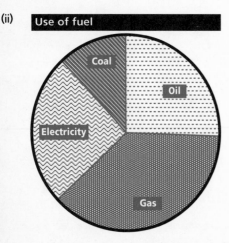

7 Using 45 litres are equal to 10 gallons we get the graph

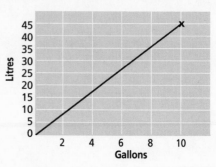

(i) 18 litres   (ii) 6 gallons   (iii) 25 litres
(iv) $7\frac{1}{2}$ gallons

8 (i) 169.9 cm (1 d.p.)   (ii) 169 cm   (iii) 162 cm

Section 10

1 a (i) 5.30 p.m.   (ii) 17.30

b 18.00 or 6.00 p.m.

c 12 hours 41 minutes

2 (i) 9.20 a.m.   (ii) 40.6 km/h (1 d.p.)

3 (i) 15 minutes   (ii) 4 minutes
(iii) 1500 m or 1.5 km   (iv) 2500 m or 2.5 km
(v) 200 m/minute

Section 11

1 **Note:** there are several correct answers to some parts of this question; these are only illustrative:
   (i) angle ABC   (ii) angle AOD   (iii) angle DOC
   (iv) angle BOA (external)   (v) angle BOD

2 (i) 60°   (ii) 120°   (iii) 300°
   (iv) 30°

3 Smaller angle is 45°.

4 $a = 132°$, $b = 115°$.

5 Angles BOE, COF, EOG, JOG, FOI and BOJ

6 (i) right-angled triangle x and y add up to 90°
   (ii) isosceles triangle x and y are equal
   (iii) equilateral triangle   AD bisects BC
                                 perpendicularly
   (iv) right-angled isosceles
        triangle x is 45°
   (v) isosceles triangle x is 70°

   (vi) obtuse-angled triangle   BC

7a Angle XZY is 44°.

b BC = 3.5 cm.

c 8 cm.

Section 12

1a $a = 35°$, $b = 26°$.

b $c = 115°$, $d = 65°$, $e = 65°$.

2 With a triangle there are no diagonals possible; with a quadrilateral there is an extra point so each corner can be joined diagonally to one other corner – so number of diagonals is number of corners times 1 divided by 2 (as a single diagonal goes to two corners). This can be built up to for the hexagon: each corner can be joined diagonally to three other corners, so number of diagonals is number of corners times 3 divided by 2 (each diagonal joins two corners).

For the nine-sided shape each corner can be joined to six other corners diagonally, so number of diagonals is 9×6 divided by $2 = 27$.

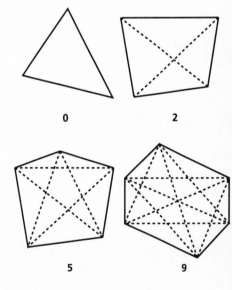

0   2

5   9

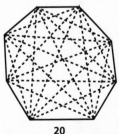

20

125

Section 13

1 (i) A is the centre – radius is 25 mm.
   (ii) BC is a chord – length is 42 mm.
   (iii) BE is a diameter – length of diameter is 49 mm.

2 **a** 4.5 cm

   b 3.14 m

   c (i) 25 cm   (ii) 157 cm or 1.57 m

   d (i) 219.8 m   (ii) 244.9 m
      (iii) Joseph runs further by 125.6 m

Section 14

1

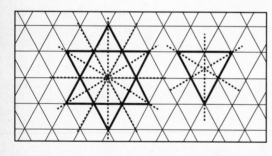

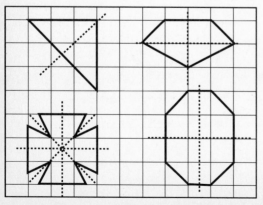

2 **a**

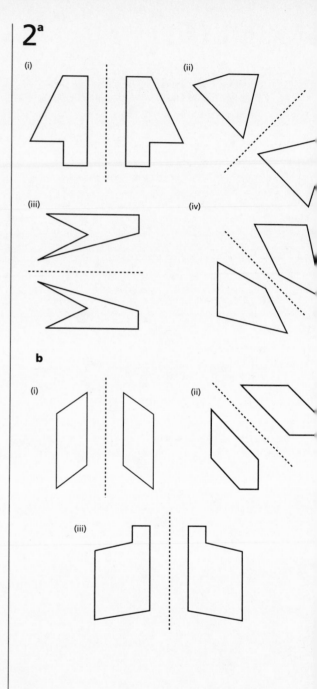

(i)   (ii)

(iii)   (iv)

b

(i)   (ii)

(iii)

3 A to A′ is 9.2 units

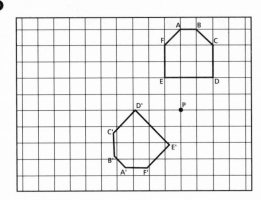

4 A′(3, 5)   B′(8, 5)   C′(8, 8)   D′(3, 8)
Length of displacement = 3.61 units

5 (i) Shape is a rectangle, rotational symmetry order 2.
(ii) Shape is a parallelogram, rotational symmetry order 2.
(iii) Shape is an octagon, with two different length sides alternating, rotational symmetry order 4.
(iv) Shape is a rhombus, rotational symmetry order 2.

6 a Scale factor is 2. The lines all pass through a common point.

b B′(12, 0)   C′(12, 12)   D′(0, 12)

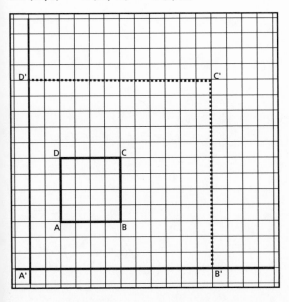

Section 15

1 (i) 64   (ii) 8

2 Prism, cube and cuboid.

3 (i) 16 cm   (ii) 16 cm²   (iii) 9 cm²
(iv) 7 cm²

4 (i) 45 m²   (ii) 14 m²   (iii) 42 m³

Section 16

1 a (i) 16   (ii) 8   (iii) 400
(iv) 4   (v) 12   (vi) 8
(vii) 32   (viii) 0

b (i) 9a   (ii) 5a   (iii) 4x + 6y
(iv) −2a² − 2a   (v) 21a²   (vi) 12x²y²

2 (i) x = 2   (ii) x = 7   (iii) x = 5
(iv) m = 2

3 a (i) 3(n − 6) = 27
(ii) The number was 15.

b (i) x + (x + 2) + (x − 4) = 46
or   3x − 2 = 46   (x = 16)
(ii) length of base = 16 cm, other sides are 12 cm and 18 cm in length.

Sample Exam Paper

1   (i) Convert 840 cm into metres.

     (ii) If a chain measures 18 cm in length, and each link is 9 mm long, how many links are there in the chain?

    (iii) How many square millimetres are there in 1 cm²?

2   Look at the following list of numbers:

        1   3   5   8   9   20   25   36   47

     (i) Write down any prime numbers in the list.

    (ii) Write down any square numbers in the list.

    (iii) Write down any three numbers, so that one of them is the difference between the other two.

3   A row of triangles is made using matchsticks as right: Nine matchsticks are used to make a row of four triangles.

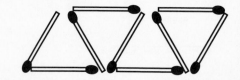

128

(i) Complete the table:

Number of triangles N	1	2	3	4	5	6
Number of matchsticks M				9		

(ii) Describe in words the pattern in the bottom line.

(iii) The rule that connects N and M is represented in the following flow chart:

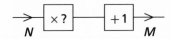

What does ? stand for?

4 Solve the equations:
  (i) $6x - 5 = 13$
  (ii) $4x - 1 = 2x + 7$

5 E X A M

  (i) Which of these letters has line symmetry?
  (ii) Which of these letters has rotational symmetry?
  (iii) What would the word look like if you looked at it using a mirror?

6 For each of the following statements, say whether the answer is *true* or *false*. In each case, justify your answers.

  (i) $693 + 587$ is about 1300.
  (ii) $4109 \div 198$ is about 200.
  (iii) 8.29×7.96 is about 64.

7 In the diagram shown alongside, calculate the values of *x*, *y* and *z*. (ABCD is a square.) Give reasons for your answers.

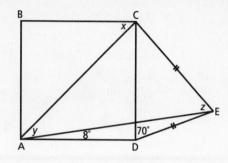

8 A bicycle wheel has a diameter of 50 cm.

    (i) Find the circumference of the wheel.

    (ii) Karl rides the bike along a road, and counts the wheel turning 300 times. How far has the bike travelled in kilometres?

9 A matchbox has dimensions 6 cm by 1 cm by 2 cm.

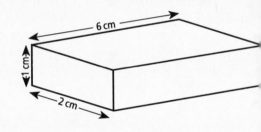

    (i) These are supplied to retailers in a packet which measures 42 cm by 5 cm by 8 cm. How many boxes of matches are in the packet?

    (ii) A match measures 3 cm by 2.5 mm by 2.5 mm. How many matches can a box hold?

0 British Rail are carrying out a survey on passengers using the trains between two stations over hourly intervals. The following numbers were recorded on 24 different occasions:

48	16	25	50	37	29
30	43	40	22	18	31
46	45	41	33	27	19
12	21	20	37	42	28

(i)   What is the range of these numbers?

(ii) Calculate the mean number of passengers per hour.

(iii) Complete the following table:

Number of passengers	Tally	Frequency
11–20		
21–30		
31–40		
41–50		
Total		24

(iv) What is the probability that on the next hour sampled, more than 30 passengers travel?

(v) Draw a pie chart to represent these data, explaining clearly how you calculated the angles.

1 Aziz has been asked to solve the equation $x^2 + 4x = 9$ by a trial and improvement method.

His first try: $1.5^2 + 4 \times 1.5 = 8.25$ Too low

Continue the working, and solve the equation correct to two decimal places.

12 Arrange the following numbers in order of size, smallest first:

$$3\frac{1}{10}, \quad \sqrt{8}, \quad \frac{25}{7}, \quad \pi$$

What is the difference between the smallest and the largest correct to two decimal places?

13 An ordinary dice (coloured red) numbered 1–6 and a tetrahedral dice (coloured blue) numbered 1–4 are rolled in a game. The score is obtained by adding the numbers on the sides that land face down.

(i) Complete the following table which shows the outcomes.

Red dice → Blue dice ↓	1	2	3	4	5	6
1						
2				6		
3						
4			7			

(ii) What is the probability that you get a score of 7?

(iii) What is the probability that you do not get a score of 7?

14 Arun, Brentwood and Crane are three towns. Arun is 40 km due north of Brentwood, and Crane is 60 km due west of Arun. Using a scale of 1 cm to represent 5 km, draw a diagram to represent their position. What is the bearing of Crane from Brentwood?

5 Copy the diagram shown on to graph (or squared) paper.

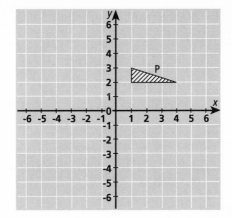

   (i) Reflect P in the *y*-axis (label it Q).

  (ii) Rotate Q by 180° about 0 (label it R).

 (iii) Reflect R in the line $y = -1$ (label it S).

 (iv) Describe how to map S on to P in one transformation.

6 A chemical is made from three components X, Y and Z. X is 20% of the weight, and Y is 35% of the weight. How much by weight of Z would be needed to make 600 kg of the chemical?

Solutions

1
(i) $840 \div 100 = 8.4\,m$
(ii) $18 \div 0.9 = 20$
(iii) $10 \times 10 = 100$

2
(i) 3, 5, 47
(ii) 1, 9, 25, 36
(iii) 5 is the difference between 3 and 8. 5, 20, 25 is another solution.

3
(i)

N	1	2	3	4	5	6
M	3	5	7	9	11	13

(ii) They increase by 2 or odd numbers starting at 3.
(iii) ? = 2 because $M = 2 \times N + 1$.

4
(i) $6x = 13 + 5 = 18$
   $\therefore \quad x = 18 \div 6 = 3$
(ii) $4x - 2x = 7 + 1$
   $\therefore \quad 2x = 8$
   $\therefore \quad x = 4$

5
(i) They all do.
(ii) X
(iii) MAXƎ

6
(i) $693 + 587 \approx 700 + 600 = 1300$ True
(ii) $4109 \div 198 \approx 4000 \div 200 = 20$ False
(iii) $8.29 \times 7.96 \approx 8 \times 8 = 64$ True

7
$x = 45°$ (symmetry of a square)
$y = 45° - 8° = 37°$ ($\angle DAC = 45°$)
$z = 40° - 12° = 28°$
   ($\angle AED = 180° - 8° - 90° - 70° = 12°$
$\therefore \quad \angle CED = 180° - 70° - 70° = 40°$)

8
(i) $\pi \times 50 = 157\,cm$
(ii) $157 \times 300 = 47\,100\,cm$

   $47\,100 \div 100\,000 = 0.471\,km$

9
(i) Volume of the packet is

   $42 \times 5 \times 8\,cm^3 = 1680\,cm^3$

   Volume of one box is

   $6 \times 2 \times 1\,cm^3 = 12\,cm^3$

   The number of boxes in the packet is

   $1680 \div 12 = 140$ boxes

(ii) Volume of one match is

   $3 \times 0.25 \times 0.25\,cm^3 = 0.1875\,cm^3$

   Hence the number of matches in one box is

   $12 \div 0.1875 = 64$ matches

10
(i) The range $= 50 - 12 = 38$
(ii) The total of the numbers $= 760$
   The mean $= 760 \div 24 = 31.7$ passengers/hour

(iii)

Number	Tally	Frequency
11–20	⊞⊞	5
21–30	⊞⊞ II	7
31–40	⊞⊞	5
41–50	⊞⊞ II	7

(iv) $\dfrac{12}{24} = \dfrac{1}{2}$
(v) $360° \div 24 = 15°$, hence the angles are
   $5 \times 15° = 75°$; $7 \times 15° = 105°$; $75°$; $105°$.
   Remember to label the sectors.

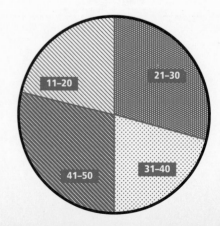

11 $x = 1.61$

12 $\sqrt{8}, 3\frac{1}{10}, \pi, \frac{25}{7}.$

The difference is

$$\frac{25}{7} - \sqrt{8} = 3.571 - 2.828$$

$$= 0.74 \quad (2\,\text{d.p.})$$

You must work with three decimal places until you get the final answer.

13 (i)

	1	2	3	4	5	6
1	2	3	4	5	6	7
2	3	4	5	6	7	8
3	4	5	6	7	8	9
4	5	6	7	8	9	10

(ii) $\dfrac{4}{24} = \dfrac{1}{6}$

(iii) $1 - \dfrac{1}{6} = \dfrac{5}{6}$

14 Bearing = 303° (Your answer should be within 2° of this.) Your triangle should have sides 12 cm and 8 cm long, i.e. twice this size.

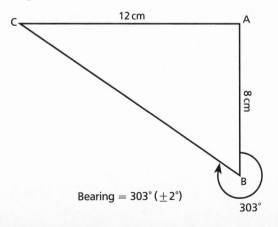

Bearing = 303° ($\pm$2°)

15 (i), (ii), (iii)

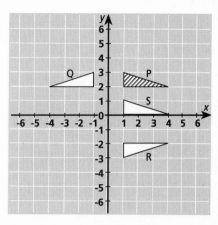

(iv) Translation $+2$ parallel to the y-axis.

16 $Z = 100\% - 35\% - 20\% = 45\%$

$$45\% \text{ of } 600\,\text{kg} = \frac{45}{100} \times 600\,\text{kg}$$

$$= 270\,\text{kg}$$

Index

U

V

W

X

Y

Titles in *The Way to Pass* series

These books are available at £7.99 each from all good bookshops or directly from Vermilion (post and packing free) using the form below, or on our credit card hotline o **0279 427203.**

ORDER FORM

National Curriculum Maths

				Quantity
Level 4	Key Stage 3	11-14 years	0 09 178116 7	....
Level 5	Key Stage 3	11-14 years	0 09 178118 3	....
Level 6	Key Stage 3	11-14 years	0 09 178125 6	....
GCSE Foundation Level	Key Stage 4	14-16 years	0 09 178123 X	....
GCSE Intermediate Level	Key Stage 4	14-16 years	0 09 178121 3	....
GCSE Higher Level	Key Stage 4	14-16 years	0 09 178127 2	....

National Curriculum English

Level 4	Key Stage 3	11-14 years	0 09 178129 9	....
Level 5	Key Stage 3	11-14 years	0 09 178135 3	....
Level 6	Key Stage 3	11-14 years	0 09 178133 7	....
GCSE	Key Stage 4	14-16 years	0 09 178131 0	....

Mr/Ms/Mrs/Miss...

Address:..

....

....

Postcode:.. Signed:...

HOW TO PAY

I enclose cheque / postal order for £........ : ....made payable to VERMILION

I wish to pay by Access / Visa card (delete where appropriate)

Card No ....Expiry date:...

Post order to **Murlyn Services Ltd, PO Box 50, Harlow, Essex CM17 ODZ.**

POSTAGE AND PACKING ARE FREE. Offer open in Great Britain including Northern Ireland. Books should arrive less than 28 days after we receive your order; they are subject to availability at time of ordering. If not entirely satisfied return in the same packaging and condition as received with a covering letter within 7 days. Vermilion books are available from all good booksellers

The Video Class Mathematics and *English* videos which accompany the above titles are available at £12.99 from leading video retailers and bookshops, or on the credit card hotline **0275 857017.**